BOOK E

Authors

Dennis McKee

Lynn Wicker

Cover Design,
Text Layout, & Graphics

Ed Francis

Illustrations

Dennis McKee

Consultants

Micheal B. Leyden, Ed.D.

Todd Fennimore, Ph.D.

Introduction To Simple And Fun Science

Science is a word which comes from a Latin term which means "to know." In order to really know, young people need to experience, to investigate, to touch, to hold, and to question. An ancient Chinese philosopher once said:

"What I hear, I forget. What I see, I remember. What I do, I know."

When young people can hear, see, and do, they can begin to understand. This book was written to encourage young people to investigate, to explore, and to question.

Education in science is a multi-faceted adventure. Young people need to learn how to "do science." This occurs as they develop Process Skills. Process Skills are methods of inquiry that help them in all academic areas of the curriculum. Some people call them "life skills" because they are used in many daily activities from baking a cake to mowing the lawn. During the process of gathering, interpreting data, and applying information about their physical and biological and earth science environment, young people master the science process skills.

These are the Process Skills we have made every attempt to nurture in this series.

Recalling	**Observing**	**Classifying**	**Setting Goals**
Measuring	**Inferring**	**Predicting**	**Gathering Data**
Graphing	**Analyzing**	**Summarizing**	**Interpreting Data**
Communicating			

As young people learn and improve their Process Skills, they are simultaneously learning the physical, biological, and earth-science content and they are involved in critical and creative problem solving. Using the Process Skills young people are enhancing and improving their critical thinking and creative thinking. They are:

- **using past observations to predict future events;**
- **performing simple experiments in an effort to find answers to questions and to develop new questions to investigate;**
- **verifying an explanation to check it out;**
- **applying knowledge and reasoning in decision making and problem solving;**
- **using science method and experience to explain observations and solve problems; and**
- **developing new questions and searching for solutions to problems.**

The Essential Learning Products Science Series encourages young people to work at their own pace. Book E is intended for young people from ages 9 through 11 years old. Use it as a supplement to existing curricula in the classroom or independently at home. Try not to impose your own conclusions.

The authors and publisher have made every reasonable effort to make sure that the activities within this book are safe when conducted as instructed. When appropriate, the authors have suggested a step be conducted by an adult and not a child. The authors and publisher assume no responsibility for any damage caused or sustained while performing the activities in this book. Supervise young readers working with the activities in this book.

Table Of Contents

What To Do As You Work Through This Book

This book is filled with fun and fascinating experiments to do. Some experiments will help you understand an idea. Some experiments will help you think of new questions. Some experiments will make you want to find out more and answer new questions.

General Safety Rules

The experiments in this book are safe but there are safety rules every scientist should learn.

1. **Pay attention to your work from start to finish.**
2. **Always clean your equipment well before and after your experiment. Always clean up after you are done experimenting.**
3. **Label your containers in experiments so you always know what they are.**
4. **When you are able, work with a partner, a friend, or an adult helper. Scientists usually work in teams.**
5. **Think about safety first.**

Here are some tips:

- Never look directly at the sun.
- Protect your eyes from anything that might splatter or shatter.
- Never get close to animals in the wild or even to pets you do not know.
- Never taste anything unless you know exactly what it is or an adult teacher, friend, or relative says it is okay.
- Stay away from fire, burners, hot water, or anything that can burn.
- Always ask an adult partner for help with the stove.
- Be very careful with scissors and ask an adult partner for help when using any cutting tool.

How To Be A Good Scientist

1. Keep a science journal. Write down your questions. Write down your observations. Draw pictures of your observations. Design your own experiments or make changes to the experiments you perform. Use graphic organizers to organize information as you uncover and discover it. Some good graphic organizers to use are shown on page 123.
2. Take your time with your experiments. Try not to hurry and try not to get frustrated. If your experiment doesn't work the first time, try again. And don't worry about failing. Every scientist makes mistakes and fails sometimes. Sometimes failures raise questions that find new solutions.
3. Keep things clean and put things away when you are done.
4. Stay organized.

Before you start any experiment:

Read through the experiment first.
Gather all the materials you will need to do the experiment together before starting.
Follow each step very carefully. Don't skip steps.

As you do your experiment:

Observe and record your results.
Be very accurate. Scientists must be accurate.
Be careful. Ask for an adult's help when suggested. Work cautiously.
Be neat. Keep your work and your work area neat.
Be creative. Think of new questions and write them down.
Make small changes in your experiment or equipment to see if the results are the same.
Make up your own experiments to answer questions. Ask an adult for advice.
Don't worry if you don't understand everything you see. There are always new things to discover.
Check references for verification. Verify what you do as often as possible.

Processes Of Science

"I roamed the countryside searching for answers to things I did not understand. Why shells existed on the tops of mountains along with imprints of coral and plants and seaweed usually found in the sea. Why the thunder lasts a longer time than that which causes it and why immediately on its creation the lightning becomes visible to the eye while thunder requires time to travel. How the various circles of water form around the spot which has been struck by a stone and why a bird sustains itself in the air. These questions and other strange phenomena engaged my thoughts throughout my life."

Leonardo da Vinci wrote this around 1500. Do you have some of the same questions Leonardo da Vinci had? What questions would you like to find the answers to?

Mr. da Vinci was a very talented person. He was an artist, a teacher, an inventor, and a scientist. He designed a spring-driven car, a life preserver, a parachute, a helicopter, and a mechanical wing for an airplane. Remember, he lived four hundred years before airplanes and helicopters were even invented. Many of his dreams and inventions did not become real until hundreds of years after he died.

Botanist, cartographer, geologist, paleontologist, mechanical engineer, ecologist, anatomist, inventor, and astronomer–Mr. da Vinci was all of these. Describe what you think each scientist might do. What other names of scientists do you know?

____

____

____

Most scientists do not work alone. Whatever scientists do today depends on the experiments, discoveries, successes, and failures of present and past scientists. Scientific ideas and information change. Here is only one example. Aristotle believed that a heavy object falls faster than a lighter object. Mr. Aristotle lived in Greece around 350 B.C. His "theory" seemed "logical" for many centuries. But, in the early 1600's, a scientist named Galileo questioned that theory. He decided to test Mr. Aristotle's idea. Supposedly, Mr. Galileo dropped two objects of the same shape but different weights from the top of the Leaning Tower of Pisa. The light object and the heavy object hit the ground at the same time. Both of these scientists were very smart. Mr. Aristotle used "LOGIC" and Mr. Galileo used "EXPERIMENT."

Do Answers Sometimes Change?

Scientists depend on evidence to support their theories. When new evidence is found that doesn't fit a theory, the theory can change—not because the scientists were wrong, but because new evidence can give scientists new ideas and new perspectives. That was a long sentence you just read, huh? Let's look at an example that might help show how theories can change.

An "Old" Theory	New Evidence	A "New" Theory
Dinosaurs were cold-blooded.	Microscopic study of bone fossils shows growth and many blood channels.	Cold-blooded animals are slow growers and have fewer blood channels. Some dinosaurs MAY have been warm-blooded.
Newborn dinosaurs were left to survive on their own.	Scientists found nests with fossils of young dinosaurs and evidence that food was brought to them in the nest.	Some adult dinosaurs may have cared for their young until they left the nest.
Dinosaurs were slow and lumbering.	Measurement of tracks and studies of bone strength show some relatively fast gaits.	Some dinosaurs may have been able to move quickly, maybe even gallop.
Most dinosaurs were huge creatures.	Small fossilized adult dinosaur bones were discovered. And footprints of dinosaurs no larger than a sparrow have been found.	Some dinosaurs may have been as small as chipmunks.

Do you think everything about dinosaurs has been found out yet?

Problem-Solving Strategy

Just like Mr. Aristotle and Mr. Galileo a long time ago, most scientists do not always look for explanations and answers in exactly the same way. But most do work through a process. They don't always follow these steps exactly the same way every time they look for answers and solutions to problems. But they usually do each step.

Problem-Solving Steps	
1. Define the problem:	What am I trying to find out?
2. Gather evidence:	What do I already know? And what else do I need to know?
3. Make a prediction:	What do I think will happen?
4. Experiment:	How can I test my prediction?
5. Gather results:	What did my experiment show?
6. Draw a conclusion:	What did I learn about the problem?
7. Raise new Questions:	What do I still not understand? What new problem does my conclusion or solution create?

Look back at the activities and experiments you've done before. Can you think of any activities or experiments in which you followed steps like these? Now, as you work through this book, remember these steps and try to follow them with every new investigation and experiment.

Techniques Of Scientists

Scientists try to work in systematic, careful ways. They have created different ways of organizing information.

Scientists use equipment to organize information. They can look at tiny atoms, distant galaxies, and the secrets of nature with modern equipment such as telescopes and electron microscopes.

Scientists organize information by very careful measurement. They are careful when they measure enormous distances between stars or the tiny dimensions of a cell.

Scientists organize information by classification. Scientists classify many objects around us. They classify things to give nature some kind of order. For example, scientists classify plants and animals. The chart on pages 20 and 21 show how plants and animals are classified today by some scientists.

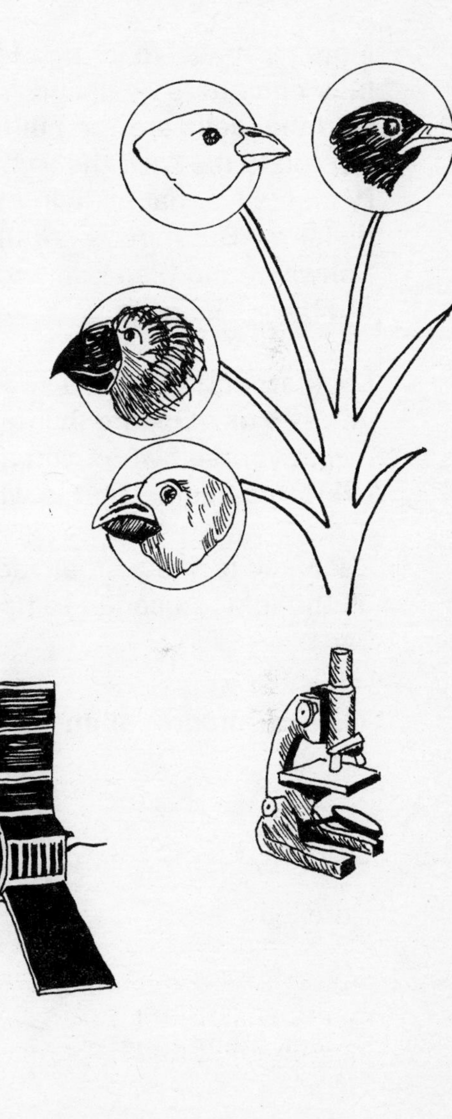

Cells: The "Building Blocks Of Living Things"

More than 300 years ago, a scientist named Robert Hooke looked at a cork and saw little chambers he called "cells." 200 years later another scientist, Theodor Schwann realized that cells are the building blocks of animals, as well as plants. Dr. Schwann helped formulate the "cell theory" that says cells are the smallest things that are alive. This theory also says that all living things are made of one or more cells that reproduce by cell division. But here is another good example of how theories can change. Since Dr. Schwann and his team wrote the "cell theory," other scientists found that fungi do not have true cells.

Look around you. You see all kinds of living and non-living things. List some things you see or think are living. List some things you see or think are not living. Don't forget yourself when you are making your lists. One or more cells make up every living organism. That is why we call cells the "building blocks" of living things.

Each cell is like a small factory where chemical reactions produce energy that helps do all the things needed to be alive. Animal cells are like microscopic, fluid-filled, closed bags.

This is a "model" of an animal cell.

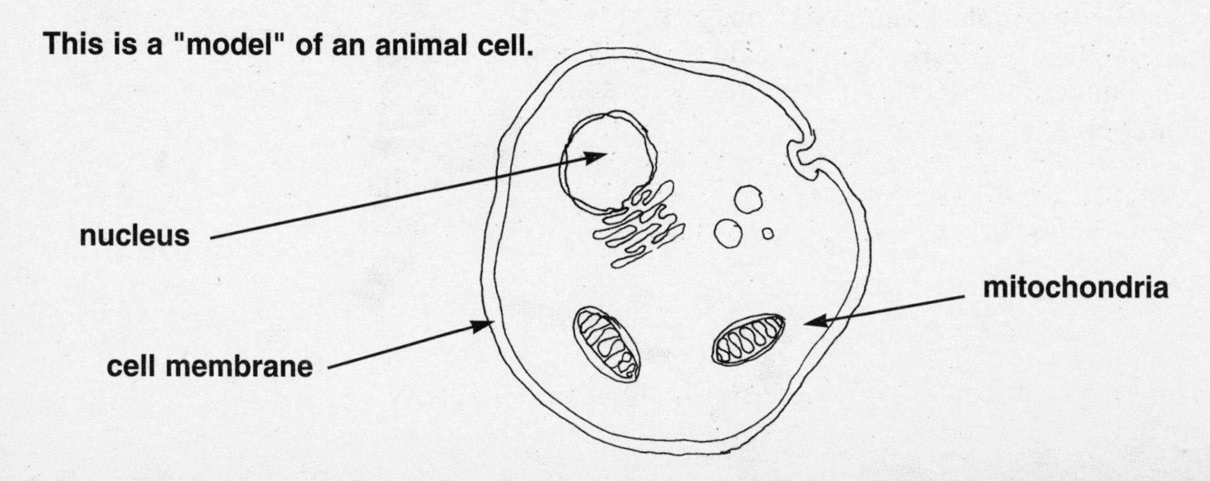

The nucleus is the "cell factory boss" that controls everything that happens in the cell. The mitochondria is the "cell factory worker" that produces energy from food.

Plant cells are like animal cells except they have a stiff cell wall. And, green plants have chloroplasts that capture the sunlight energy to make food.

Some living things, such as bacteria, are only one cell. Other living things, like people, are made up of trillions of cells.

This is a "model" of a plant cell.

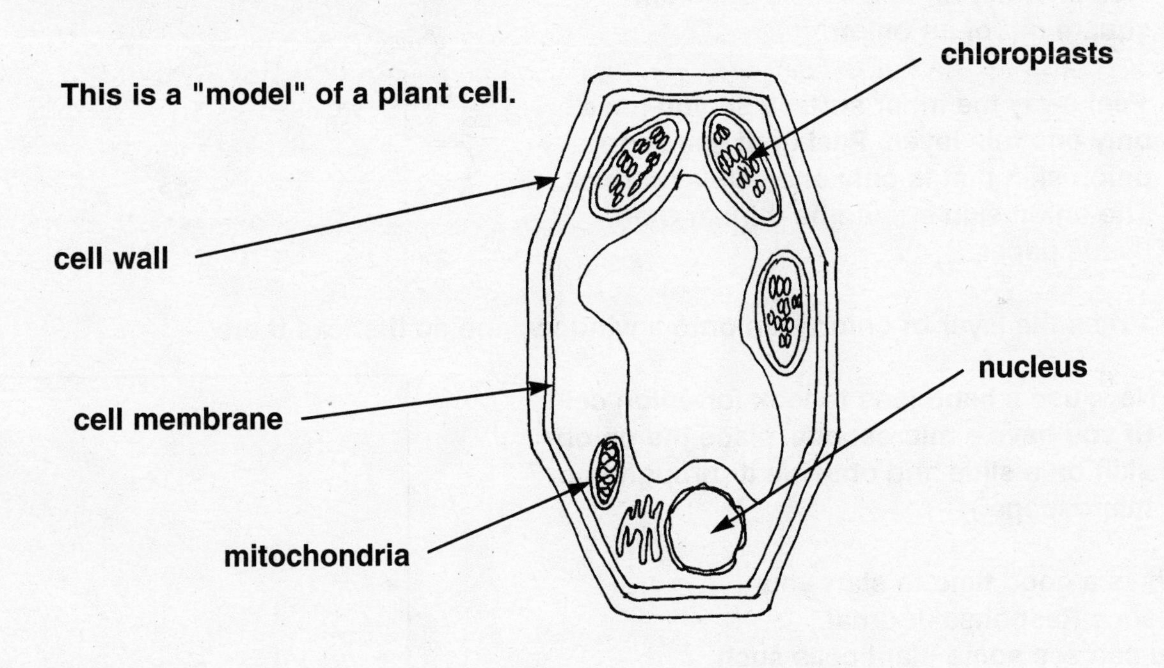

What is different between this plant cell and the animal cell?
What is the same between this plant cell and the animal cell?

Let's See If We Can See A Cell

What you need:

a hand lens (or microscope, if available)
an onion
paper or a science journal

What to do:

1. Ask an adult to help slice a one-inch square out of an onion.

2. Peel away the inner surface so you have only one thin layer. Peel until you have onion skin that is only one-cell-layer thick. The onion skin should be thinner than tissue paper.

3. Press the layer of onion skin onto a windowpane so it sticks there.

4. Now, use a hand lens to look for onion cells. (If you have a microscope, place the onion skin on a slide and observe it through your microscope.)

This is a good time to start your Science Response Journal.
You can see some plant cells such as onion cells with a hand lens.
You need a microscope to see animal cells.

Draw what you see.

A Homemade Microscope

If you don't have a hand lens or a microscope, you can make a simple water microscope. Here's how.

What you need:

- a plastic cottage cheese container
- scissors
- plastic wrap
- a rubber band
- water
- objects to study, including your onion skin

What to do:

1. Cut a hole in the side of the container. Make sure the hole is large enough to fit fingers into the container.
2. Stretch plastic wrap over the mouth of the container. Push the plastic wrap into the container, only slightly.
3. Attach the plastic wrap to the container with the rubber band.
4. Carefully pour water on top of the plastic wrap so that a pool of water forms.
5. Look at a hair. Look at a seed, a flower petal. Look at your onion skin. Describe and draw what you see.

Osmosis

Water enters a cell from the outside. Water travels through the cell membrane by a process called osmosis.

Okay, let's stop for a minute to remind you that sometimes words might slip in that you don't know yet. It's a good idea to have a dictionary near you for when that happens. What is a cell membrane? A cell membrane is the thin skin that surrounds cells. Water crosses the cell membrane to where there is less water or more dissolved substances such as salt or sugar. This movement of water into and out of cells is called osmosis.

Observe Osmosis In A Potato

What you need:

2 potatoes
sugar
3 dishes
a spoon
a knife

What to do:

1. Ask an adult helper to cut two potatoes into equal halves. Throw one piece away or save it for dinner not to be wasteful. You will only need three halves for this experiment.

2. Ask your adult helper to peel away a 1/2-inch strip of skin at the base of each potato.

3. Cut a one-inch square hollow in the curved side of each potato.

4. Put one potato half, flat-side down in a dish of water. Number this potato, POTATO #1. Put the second potato half, flat-side down in a second dish of water. Number this potato POTATO # 2.

5. Ask your adult helper to help you boil the third potato half for ten minutes to kill the cells. Let this potato cool for five minutes. Place it flat-side down in a third dish of water and mark it POTATO # 3.

- Potato # 1 is your control potato. Leave it as it is to compare to the others.
- Potato # 2 shows how water moves through living cells. Put a spoonful of sugar in the hollow.
- Potato # 3 shows how water moves through dead cells. Put a spoonful of sugar in the hollow.

Let your experiment set for one day. Examine it tomorrow.
Describe what happened. What happened without the sugar?
What happened to the potato with the dead cells?
What happened to the potato with the living cells and the sugar?

A potato is a plant and like other plants it's built of cells. The following pages show the classification of other plants. Where do you think a potato might fit?

Plant And Animal Classification Chart

This chart is a simple chart that shows the main classification of plants and animals. If possible, get a good plant book from the library to help you learn more about the different kinds of plants and plant classification. When you get to more investigation of animals, a good book about animals will help, too.

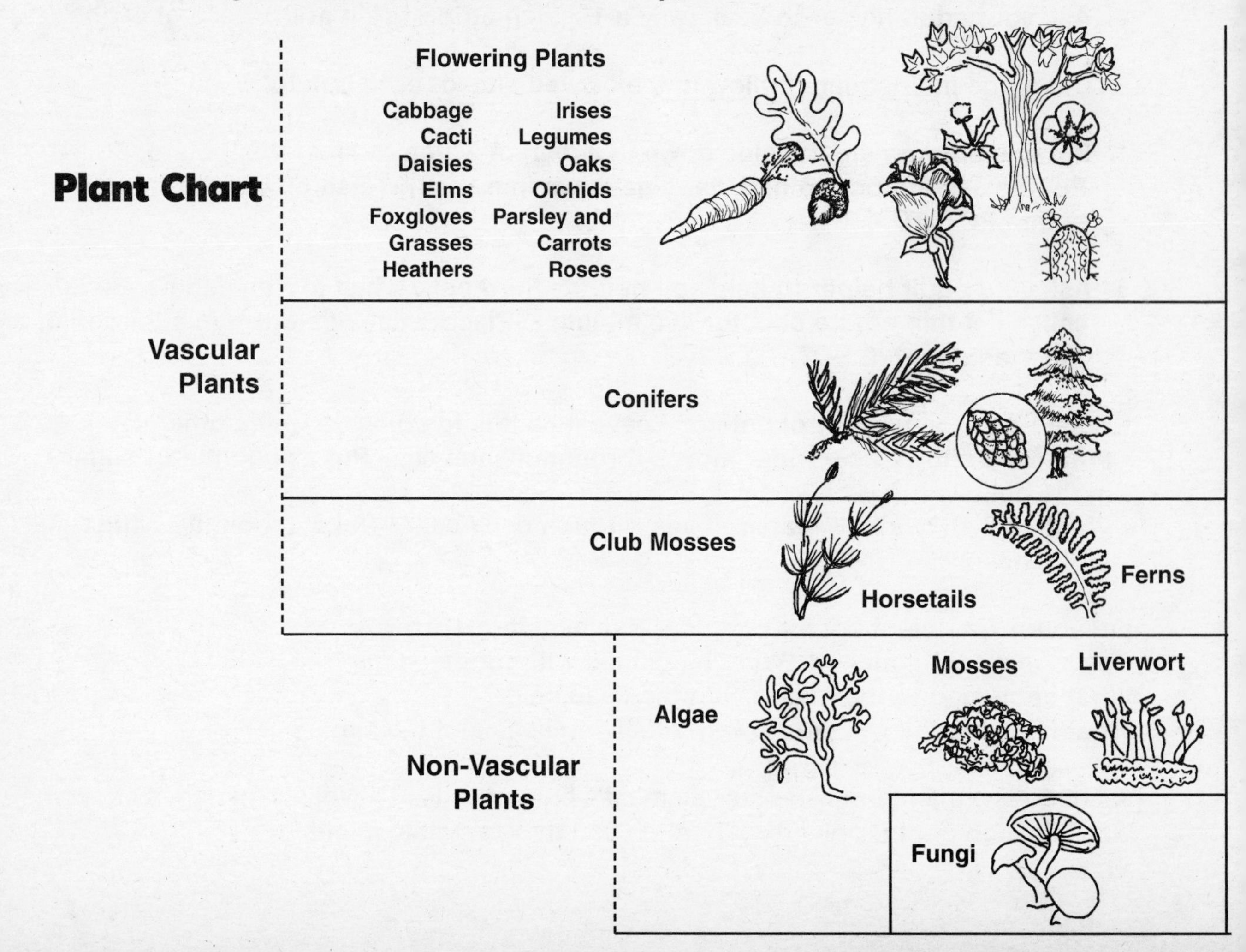

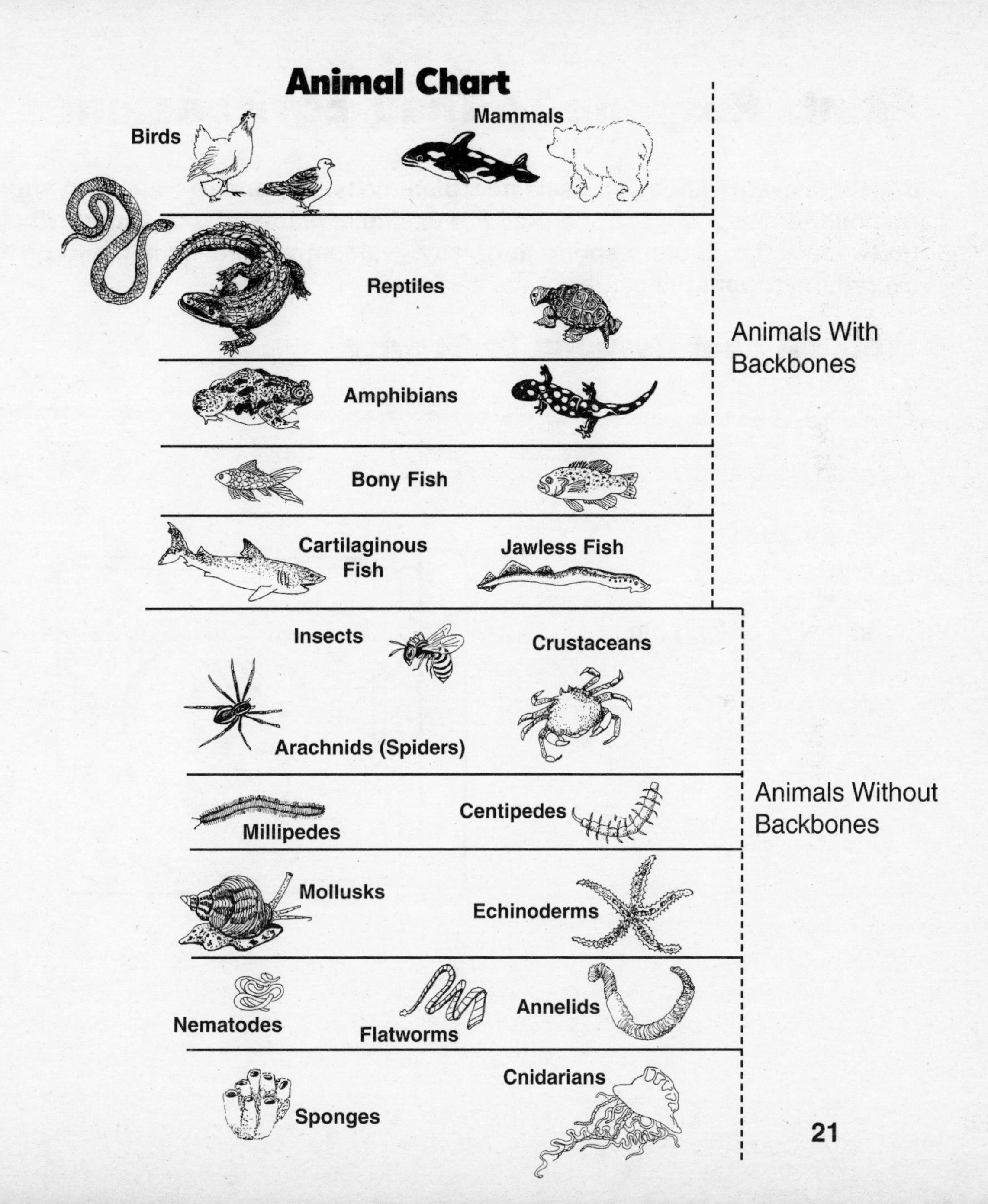
Animal Chart
Birds
Mammals
Reptiles
Amphibians
Bony Fish
Cartilaginous Fish
Jawless Fish
Animals With Backbones
Insects
Crustaceans
Arachnids (Spiders)
Millipedes
Centipedes
Animals Without Backbones
Mollusks
Echinoderms
Nematodes
Flatworms
Annelids
Sponges
Cnidarians

Plants Respond To Their Environment

In your last experiment, you saw how plant cells respond to water and sugar. Plants respond to many things in nature. For example, plants respond to gravity. Plant roots grow down. The roots respond to gravity. Remember, gravity is the force that pulls everything toward the center of the earth.

Watch A Root Respond To Gravity

What you need:

- bean
- cork
- cotton balls
- glue
- jar with lid
- stiff wire or long pin

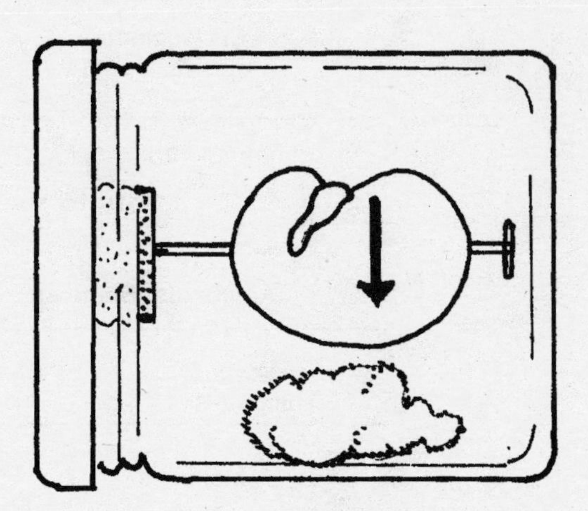

What to do:

1. Soak the bean in a cup of water for 24 hours.
2. Glue the cork to the lid of the jar.
3. Push the wire or pin through the bean as shown. Push the wire or pin into the cork.
4. Put the cotton in the jar and water it.
5. Screw the lid onto the jar as shown.
6. Lay the jar on its side. Make sure it does not roll.
7. When the root is about 1/2–inch long, write down which way it is growing. Draw a picture of your seed.
8. Turn the jar over and see what happens to the root.

Record your observations. How long did it take the 1/2–inch root to grow? What happened when you turned the jar over?

Don't waste the seed you started rooting here. Get a pot or milk carton filled with soil and plant your rooting seed about a half inch under the soil. It should be easy to see which end is up now that the root and the stem are starting to develop. Which do you think should be planted in the soil and which should be above the soil in the sunlight?

Plants Respond To Light

The roots grow down but the stems and leaves of plants respond to light. Plants need light to live.

If you are just starting to grow your plants, this activity may take several weeks. To start your bean plants growing, soak three bean seeds in water for 24 hours. Plant them about 1/2–inch under the soil in three different pots. Mark your pots, #1, #2, #3 and set them in a window until the green leaves are growing. Then you're ready for this experiment. Until your plants are growing, you can go ahead with the next four experiments then come back to this one.

Watch Your Plants' Different Responses

What you need:

- 3 small bean plants in pots
- 2 shoe boxes with lids
- a piece of cardboard
- masking tape
- scissors
- graph paper
- a pencil or pen

What to do:

1. Cut a hole in the top of one shoe box. Look at the picture and put the hole close to the side, not in the middle. Label the box Plant # 1.

2. Make a plant maze in the second box. Do this by taping pieces of cardboard on the inside of the box. Look at the picture to see how. Cut a hole near the top of the shoe box. Cut the hole as close to the middle as you can. Label this shoe box Plant # 2.

3. Plant # 3 will not have a shoe box. It is your control plant.

4. Place Plant # 1 in Box # 1.

5. Place Plant # 2 in Box # 2.

6. Place Box # 1, Box #2, and Plant # 3 on a well-lighted window ledge. Make sure you give them each the same amount of water each day.

Draw pictures of your plants on your graph paper. Record their growth and your observations.

How did the plants respond to light? ______________________________

What differences in the leaves of the plants did you observe? ______________

How can you explain those differences? ______________________________

____

How does this experiment help you decide where to plant plants outside? How does this experiment help you decide where to place indoor, houseplants in your home?

____

Trees Don't Mind Telling Their Age

Look at some trees growing around you. Like most plants, even large trees are shaped partly by their surroundings. For example, trees in a dense forest sometimes have to grow very tall to reach the light. Some trees on very windy hills or on the windy seashore are shaped by the wind. Tell how trees you have seen were shaped by their surroundings.

___

___

It's not real polite to ask how old Grandma or Granddad are but you can certainly find out how old the trees in your neighborhood are. How old are some of the trees in your neighborhood?

Tree Birthdays

What you need:

a measuring tape
trees

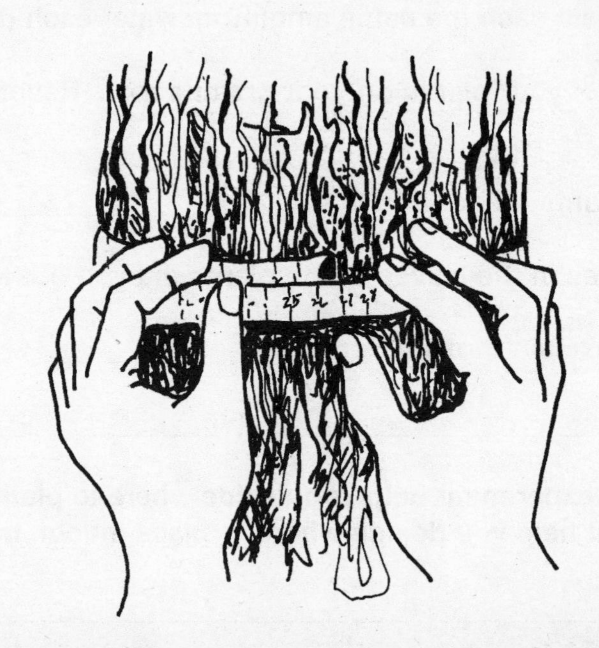

What to do:

1. Measure around the trunk of a tree at about 5 feet.

2. You just measured the circumference of the tree trunk. Now to figure out its age. Divide the circumference by 1–inch.

3. Find several trees of different sizes in your area and do steps 1 and 2 again.

4. Write down the age you think some of the trees where you live are. Which do you estimate is the youngest? Which do you estimate is the oldest?

____

Here's a challenge. Draw the circumference of one or more of the trees you measured. Now try to figure out what the diameter of each is. First, do you know what circumference and diameters are? Do you have your dictionary?

Many trees in North America grow about one inch onto their circumference each year. Trees such as maple trees, oak trees, some fruit trees, elm trees (trees that grow in temperate climates) add about one inch to their circumference each year.

Not all trees grow at that rate, though. Redwoods and some fir trees add more than one inch to their circumference. Trees such as yews and chestnut trees don't always grow as much. Do you live where there are palm trees? A palm tree can grow taller without growing fatter, relative to its height.

There we go with another new phrase. What do you think the phrase "relative to its height" means? How can you find out?

____

____

Giant "Drinks Of Water!"

Sometimes it's hard to believe that trees as tall as the giant redwoods can move water all the way from their roots in the earth to their leaves. But they do. They are called vascular plants. The vascular plants are flowering plants which include some trees, conifers (which are trees whose seeds grow inside protective cones), ferns, and horsetails. Vascular plants have true leaves and roots and special channels in their stems that carry water and other substances through the plant.

Plants wilt when they don't have enough water. Even the limbs of tall trees will wilt when they don't have enough water. Water filling plant cells causes pressure called turgor pressure. That pressure keeps plants from wilting. Let's see if we can increase turgor pressure in a celery stalk.

Stand A Celery Stalk At Attention

What you need:

- wilted stalk of celery
- a drinking glass
- water
- food coloring
- a balloon

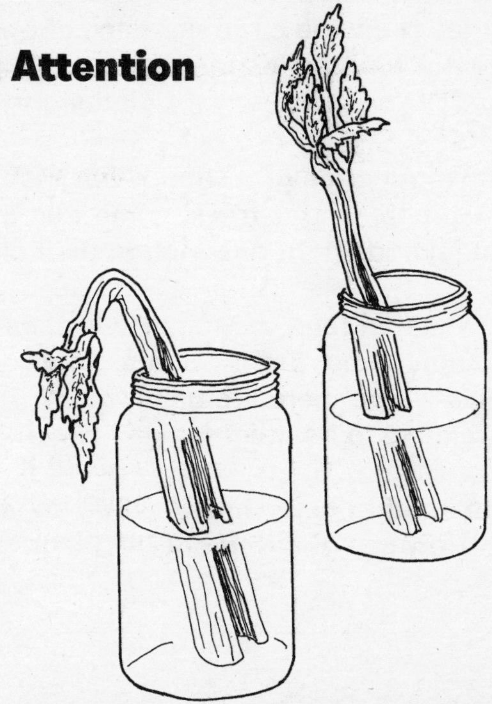

What to do:

1. Place a stalk of celery on the counter overnight without any water.

2. When it is wilted, ask an adult helper to cut a 1/2-inch slice off the bottom. This will open the vascular system.

3. Put enough food coloring in the water to make the water a dark color. You can use different colors in different glasses to see if color makes a difference. If you change the colors in different experiments what do you call the colors?
   (Hint: You are varying the colors.)

   ____

4. Stand the wilted celery stalk in the glass of water overnight.

   Write what you observed. What do you think the water might be filling up that makes the celery stand firm again? (Hint: Think back to your experiment with the potato and osmosis.)

   ____

   ____

5. Try another experiment to demonstrate how turgor pressure works. Fill your balloon with water. Describe it. Now release about half the water in the balloon. Now describe it. How do you think your balloon is a little like cells in a plant? How do you think the balloon is very different from plant cells?

   ____

   ____

Design An Experiment

Now, design your own experiment to investigate the effects of turgor pressure on plants. Use your Science Journal to write "What you need" and "What to do."
Here's a model to follow.

My Experiment To Test Turgor Pressure

What I need:

____

____

____

What to do:

1.

2.

3.

4.

My Illustration

My Results:

____

____

____

____

Water Enters And Leaves Leaves

Do plants sweat? Well, not exactly like we do but they do loose excess water through their leaves. Water evaporates through holes or pores called stomata. Some large trees lose as many as 200 or more gallons of water each day. How can you prove that water evaporates from a plant's leaves? Let's make a model and see.

Plants' Leaves Release Water

What you need:

a growing plant (The bean plants you grew to observe reaction to light will work.)
tape
plastic sandwich bag

What to do:

1. Place your plant in a sunny window. Water it.

2. Tape the plastic sandwich bag over one or two leaves.

3. After three hours in the sun, observe your plant.

Describe what you see. Where do you think the water on the inside of the plastic bag came from? Did you know large trees can release as much as 15,000 pounds of water in 12 hours? How do you think that might affect the humidity near the tree? First find out what humidity is. How can you find out? When you find out, explain in your science journal what humidity is.

How humid does it get where you live. Do you have humidity indexes or heat indexes at some times in the year? How do you think humidity affects temperature? How can you find out?

Design Your Own Experiment

Okay, did you demonstrate that water evaporates from a leaf? How do you think you can measure how much water a leaf actually loses? Before you read any further, try to design your own experiment to see if you can find a way to measure how much water a leaf loses. Write what you will need and what your steps are in your science journal. Then try your experiment.

My Experiment To Measure Water Loss In Leaves

What I need:

____

____

____

What to do:

1.

2.

3.

4.

My Illustration

My Results:

____

____

____

Another Experiment

After you tried your own experiment, try this one. Then answer: which experiment do you think worked better? Could you measure the loss of water from either experiment? If you invented a better way to measure the loss of water, send your idea to us.

Another Way To Measure Water Loss In Leaves

What you need:

- twig with leaves
- 2 glasses or clear cups
- ruler
- cooking oil
- water
- paper or your science journal
- magic marker

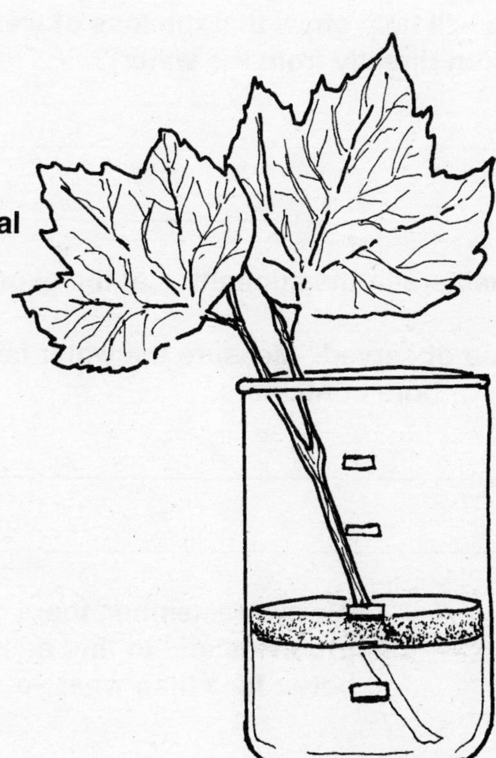

What to do:

1. Use your ruler and measure inches on the sides of the glasses (cups). Tape a paper marker at each inch level. Beakers will be more accurate if you have them.

2. Pour 3–inches of water into each container. Put the twig in one of the containers.

3. Pour a little bit of cooking oil into the container with the twig. Pour only enough oil to form a layer over the water. Water cannot evaporate through oil. How do you think this will help show that the loss of water is through the stem and leaves (not evaporation directly from the water)?

____

____

4. Put both containers in the sunlight. Let the experiment stand for at least 10 hours.

   Write what you observed. Measure the water level in both containers. Compare the level of water in both containers.

____

____

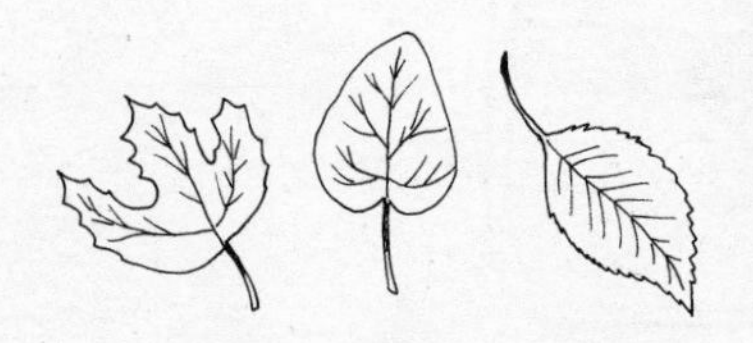

Always remember, there can be many different ways to solve problems and to find answers. Often, you probably have a better idea than what you read in a book. So try to be creative.

Plants Need Water And Sunlight, Too

Do you remember reading that Earth is sometimes called the "water planet?" Most of Earth is covered by water. And most of the water that covers Earth is ocean water, oceans that are filled with fascinating creatures. Living creatures, both plants and animals, live at different depths in the ocean. Green plants need sunlight so they live where the sun can reach them. They need sunlight to make food.

What Happens When The Sun Is Taken Away From Plants?

What you need:

a small cooking pot
a plot of grass

What to do:

1. First, get an adult helper's permission for this experiment.
2. Place the pot upside down on the grass.
3. Leave the pot on the grass for a week.
4. At the end of the week, lift the pot. Compare the color of the grass under the pot to the rest of the grass. Describe the grass under the pot. Describe the grass around the pot.

Plants need sunlight to make their own food. The green in plants is caused by chlorophyll. Remember the word chloroplasts from the beginning of this book. Well, chlorophyll is the chemical in chloroplasts that captures the sun's energy. Without sunlight, chlorophyll is not produced. Without chlorophyll the plant can't make food. So, without sunlight, plants will die. This is why marine plants grow in the ocean's sunlight zone.

Animals

As with plants, it would be helpful to get a good book about animals from the library. Then you can learn more about the many different kinds of animals and how they are classified.

Invertebrates

Invertebrates are animals without backbones. These are some invertebrates.

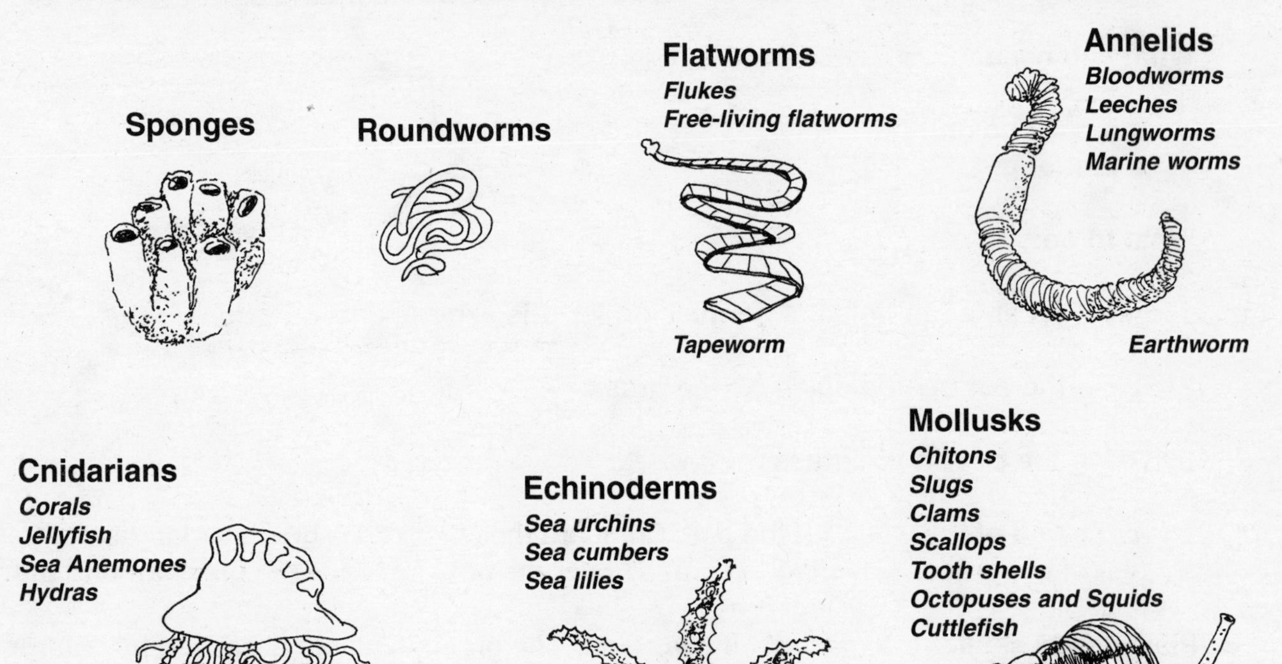

More Invertebrates

Arthropods are invertebrates with jointed bodies that have an "outside skeleton" called an exoskeleton.

Millipedes

Centipedes

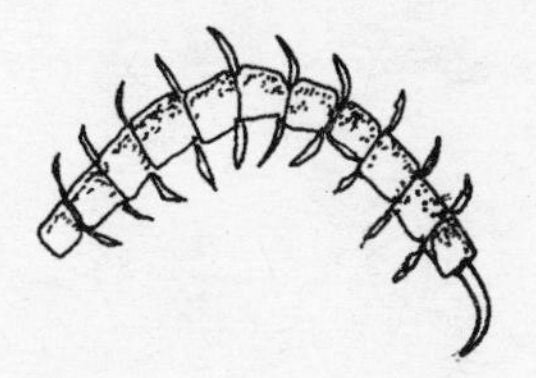

Crustaceans

Water fleas
Wood lice
Lobsters
Fish lice
Barnacles

Crab

Insects

Springtails
Silverfish and Bristletails
Dragonflies and Damselflies
Butterflies and Moths
Grasshoppers and Crickets
Earwigs
Stick insects
Cockroaches
Mantids
Termites
Lice
True bugs
Thrips
Lacewings
Beetles
Flies
Fleas

Ant

Arachnids

Scorpions
Mites
Harvestmen

Spider

Bee

Vertebrates are animals with backbones.

Jawless Fish

Cartilaginous Fish

Rays

Shark

Bony Fish

Coelacanth and Lungfish
Birchirs
Sturgeons and Paddlefish
Eels
Herrings and Anchovies
Salmon and Trout
Carp and Catfish
Perch, Marlin, Swordfish, and Tuna
Anglerfish
Cod
Flying fish
Grunion
Sticklebacks

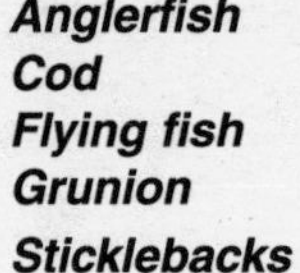

Seahorse

Goldfish

Bass

Amphibians

Frogs
Salamanders
Caecilians

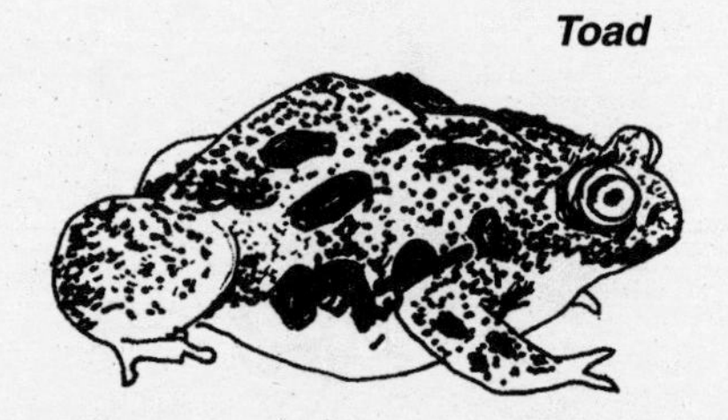

Toad

Newt

More Vertebrates

Alligator

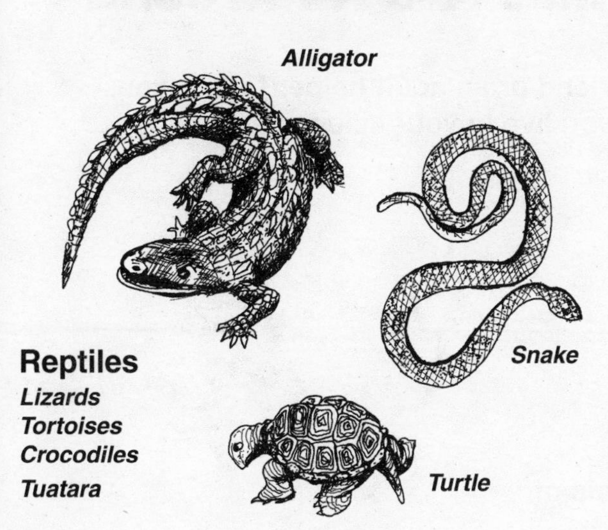

Snake

Reptiles

Lizards
Tortoises
Crocodiles
Tuatara

Turtle

Birds

Divers
Grebes
Albatrosses and Petrels
Penguins
Pelicans, Gannets, and Cormorants
Herons and Storks
Ducks, Geese, and Swans
Eagles, Hawks, and Vultures
Pheasants and Partridges
Gulls and Plovers
Doves
Parrots
Cuckoos and Roadrunners
Owls
Hummingbirds
Kingfishers, Bee-eaters, and Rollers
Perching Birds

Pigeon

Chicken

Mammals

Platypus

Egg-laying Mammals

Duck-billed Platypus
Echidnas

Marsupials

(mammals raised in the mother's pouch)
Opossums
Koalas
Bandicoots
Kangaroos and Wallabies

Kangaroo

Placental Mammals

(mammals nourished in the mother's placenta before birth)
Hedgehogs, Shrews, and Moles
Bats
Rabbits and Hares
Anteaters and Armadillos
Rodents
Dolphins
Dogs and Cats
Seals, Sea Lions, and Walruses
Hyraxes
Manatees and Dugongs
Horses, Tapirs, and Rhinoceroses
Pigs, Deer, Sheep, Antelope, and Cattle
Lemurs, Monkeys, and Apes
People

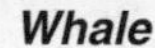

Whale

Bear

Elephant

Different Plants And Animals Are All Around

Take a nature hike. You might want to invite a friend or an adult helper to join you. Start recording the living things around where you live in your science journal.

What you need:

the "Nature Hike" checklist
a science journal or notebook
a pencil

What to do:

1. Take a walk and look very carefully for animals or "signs" of animals.

2. Write and draw what you observe in your journal. Remember, you don't have to see an animal to know one was there. What kinds of "signs" could tell you an animal was there? Write down any signs you see. Are there any signs you can observe with other senses than your eyesight?

Even though our emphasis will be on animals as we begin to investigate them, write down both the plants and animals you observe on your nature hikes. Yes, hikes. Take as many nature hikes as you like. You'll see different living things at different times of the day and at different times of the year. Besides, it's good exercise, too.

Nature Hike Checklist

Name ______________________________ Date ____________________

Location____________________________ Weather ____________________

Animals Observed

____

____

____

Signs Of Animals

Check what you see. Then draw it in the appropriate box.

___webs ___insect eggs ___nests ___holes in the ground

___bird droppings ___bird eggs ___spider eggs ___smells

___trails ___holes in leaves ___egg cases ___holes in trees

___tracks ___sounds ___shed skins ___paths

___food remains ___other ___other ___other

Tiny Animals Are Around You

Sometimes you have to look real hard to see animals around you. Let's look for some very small animals, animals that sometimes you don't even notice unless they "bug" you.

Does that hint help you guess what some of those tiny animals might be?
Before you continue, try predicting what kind of tiny animals you might find in the soil around where you live.

Now, see how close you were with your predictions.

A Tiny Animal Collector

What you need:

- a funnel
- a jar
- a lamp
- soil from a yard
- a small box for soil (a shoe box)

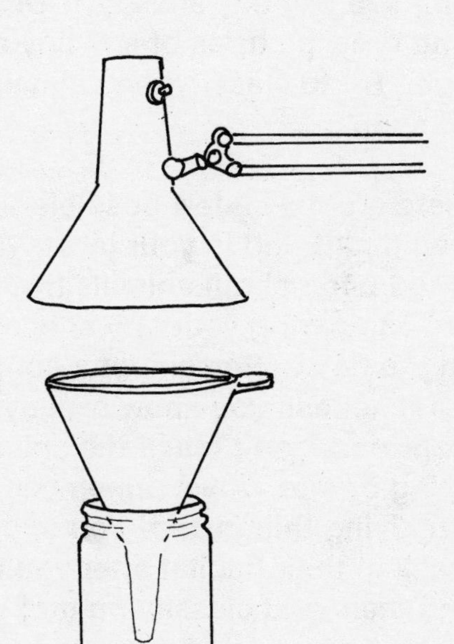

What to do:

1. Place the funnel in the jar.
2. Collect soil from outside in a container. Any container that will hold about 2 cups of soil will work.
3. Pour the soil into the funnel until it is full.
4. Place your apparatus near a lamp that will help to warm the soil.

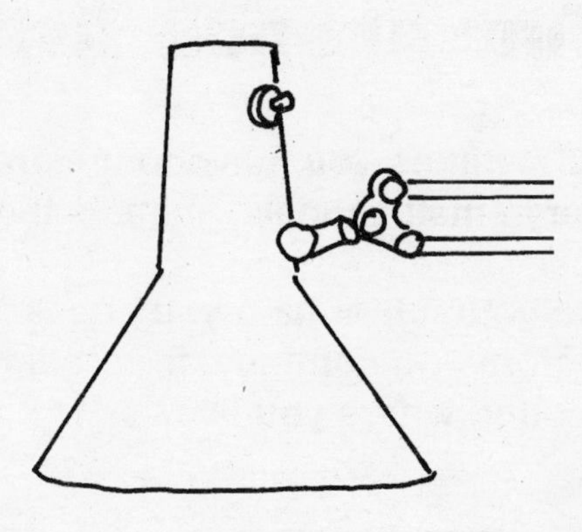

After about an hour, look inside the jar. Can you see any tiny animals? Describe them and draw pictures of any tiny animals you see. Try to classify the animals you see in the cup.

Here are only a few possible tiny animals you might find in your jar. If you have a good book about animals from the library, try comparing your tiny animals with those in the book. Remember a couple issues. First, unless you know exactly what you captured, don't touch the animal. It could sting or bite. Also, remember tiny animals are living things, too. You should put them back in their habitat after you finish observing them and classifying them.

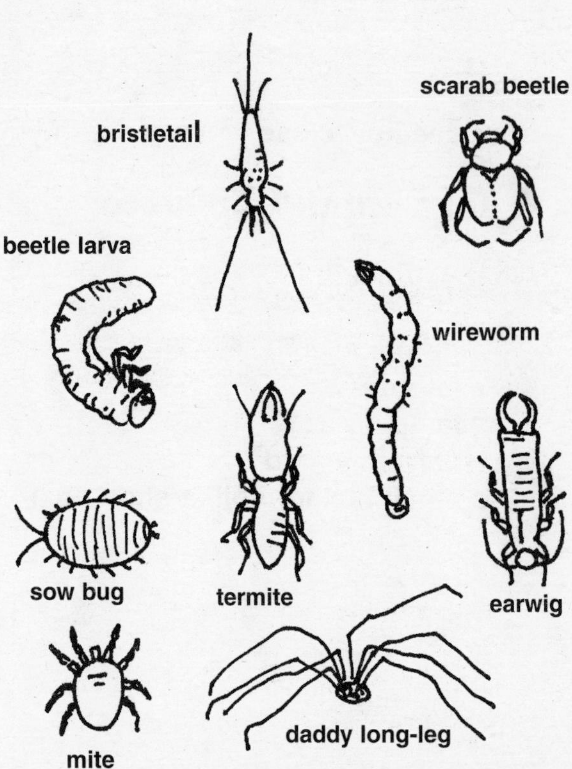

Animals Can Swim, Sink, And Float

Most marine plants need sunlight to survive. Can you infer where most marine plants live in the oceans? It is called a zone. Try to infer the name of the zone where most marine plants live.

The ____________ zone.

Like water plants, animals that live in the water come in all shapes and sizes. But they also move through the water and live at many different depths. They move in different ways. Some animals like the Portuguese Man-Of-War are moved by the currents and waves. But most animals that live in both fresh and saltwater move on their own.

Marine animals are animals that live in saltwater. One kind of marine animal includes mammals such as dolphins and whales. Another kind of marine animal is fish such as swordfish and tuna. Some swim very fast such as a swordfish. They can swim almost 70 miles per hour usually in search of food. Most animals that live in water all the time have fins that help them swim and keep them from rocking from side to side. Most fish have a swim bladder that helps them float. Let's simulate how a swim bladder can help a fish move up and down in the water.

Simulate A Swim Bladder

What you need:

- a large jar or large bowl
- water
- 2 marbles
- 2 round balloons

What to do:

1. Half-fill the bowl or jar with water.

2. Put a marble in each balloon.

3. Tie a knot as close to the marble as you can in one balloon.

4. Place the balloon in the water. Describe what happens.

5. Blow the other balloon up so it is about twice as big as the uninflated balloon. Tie a knot to keep the air inside.

6. Place this balloon in the water. Describe what happens. If it doesn't float the first time add a little more air until it does.

A swim bladder in a fish acts like the balloon. It fills with air and two things happen. One is that the air in the swim bladder makes the fish more buoyant. There's another one of those big words. Find out what the word buoyant means. Do you know what a buoy is? That's a start. The second thing the swim bladder does is make the fish larger. It blows the fish up so the surface of the fish is larger and there is more area for water to push the fish upwards.

What kinds of things do people use to float in water? Are any of the things people use to float in water similar to a fish's swim bladder? What could you design to help you sink and float like a fish? Suppose you discovered a sunken treasure ship. What could you design like a fish's swim bladder that could help you raise the ship to the surface?

The Depths Animals Go To

Some animals that live in water can swim very deep. Some stay closer to the surface or near the shore. But water animals, both marine and fresh water animals, adjust to the different depths in rivers, in lakes, or in the ocean. The pressure in water gets stronger as you swim deeper. Have you ever felt pressure in your ears as you swam to the bottom of a pool? Pressure is the force applied over a certain area. Since water has weight, it causes pressure. As water depth increases, so does water pressure. Let's compare the pressure of water at different levels.

Water Pressure Varies By Depth

What you need:

- a pencil
- a pitcher
- water
- a paper cup
- masking tape

What to do:

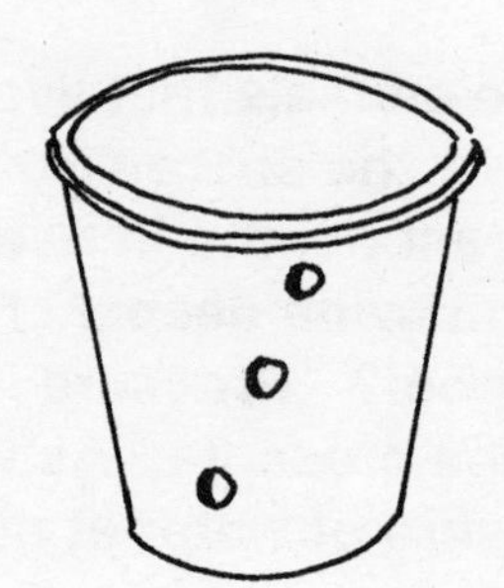

1. Ask an adult helper to punch three holes the same size in the cup. The holes should be at the top, the middle, and near the bottom of the cup. Notice in the drawing that the holes should not be directly above each other. They should be slightly diagonal.

2. Cover the holes with masking tape.

3. Set the cup on the edge of a sink.

4. Fill the pitcher with water.

5. Ask your helper to keep pouring water into the cup while you remove the tape.

6. Measure the stream of water coming out of each hole. With your measurements, decide where in the cup the pressure is the greatest.

Write what happens.
Which stream squirts out the farthest?
Which stream squirts out the shortest?
Why do you think so?

Hint: Remember, water pressure increases with depth.

Reflecting On Learning

Okay, let's get a little off the subject for a minute. This is a good place to mention the different kinds of sciences. We've discussed many different kinds of scientists: botanists, chemists, biologists, ecologists, physicists, astronomers, and on and on. But it's important to realize that the sciences like earth science, life science, and physical science are not separate areas. They really are integrated. Now, there's a word you should look up. Do you have your dictionary? I'll wait a minute while you look that word up and write down what it means.

Okay, where were we? Oh, yes, the last few activities you did are a good example of how sciences are integrated. Let's think about that for a minute. First, you learned a little about how water animals use a swim bladder to float and how they adjust to pressure– Life Science, right?

But you also learned a little bit about water pressure and buoyancy and how pressure can actually push water out of a cup– Physical Science, right? And you learned a little about the oceans, ocean depths and the sunlight zone– Earth Science. But let's not stop there.

What else did you learn and do? Well, you did some reading, right?...and some writing, right? So your language arts skills were also integrated as you learned more about science. And there's more. You did some calculations, didn't you? You measured how far the water moved and you calculated where the pressure was the greatest in the cup. You might even have done some illustrating.

What do you think this all says about learning?

Think about all the different areas involved as you continue your adventures in learning.

Fish Are Cold-Blooded Animals

Fish are cold-blooded animals. Their body temperature changes depending on the temperature around them. But mammals are warm-blooded. They stay about the same temperature no matter what the outside temperature is. Water can be very cold, especially in deeper water where less sunlight reaches. Fish get cold down there, but mammals stay warm. Mammals have fat, sometimes called blubber that keeps them warm. Let's simulate a whale's blubber and see if fat can affect temperature.

Fat Insulates

What you need:

2 paper cups
2 thermometers (used for taking temperatures in people)
cotton balls
cooking oil
a timer

What to do:

1. Place a thermometer in one empty cup.

2. Put a layer of cotton balls on the bottom of the second cup. Place the thermometer in the cup so the bulb is resting on the cotton balls. Fill the rest of the cup with cotton balls.

3. Record the temperature when you begin.

4. Pour cooking oil into the cup filled with cotton balls. Make sure the cotton balls are well soaked with cooking oil.

5. Place both cups in the freezer.

6. After 30 minutes, remove the cups and record the temperature of each thermometer.

Compare the temperatures. How do you think this experiment demonstrates that fat insulates from the cold? What part of a whale do you think you can compare the cooking oil to? How do you think this experiment demonstrates how blubber in whales helps them stay warm?

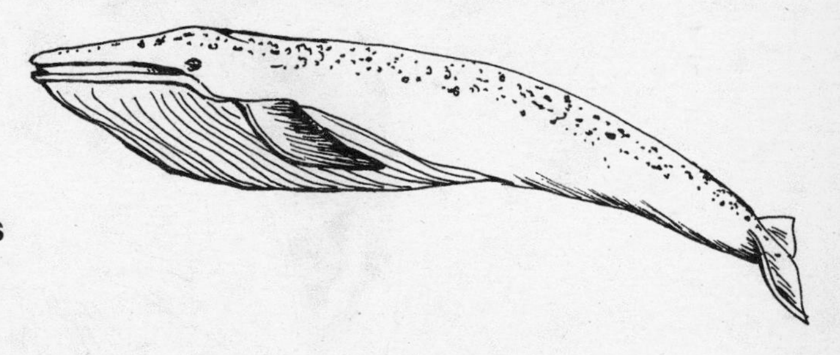

There are cold-blooded and warm-blooded animals that live on land, too. Investigate what some of the other cold-blooded animals are. What other animals are warm-blooded?

Earth

The ocean is only one part of our Earth. True, it takes up nearly 70% of the surface of Earth. But there is a lot more to Earth. The oceans are a part of the Earth's crust, the outer-most core. Have you ever peeled an apple? The apple peel is only a very thin covering of the apple. Similarly, the outer crust of the Earth is only a thin layer. Earth has several layers: the crust, the mantle, the outer core, and the inner core.

Earth's crust is 4 miles deep under the deepest part of the oceans but about 22 miles deep under land. The mantle is about 1,800 miles deep. The outer core is about 1,240 miles deep. And the core is about 850 miles to its center most point, the very center of Earth.

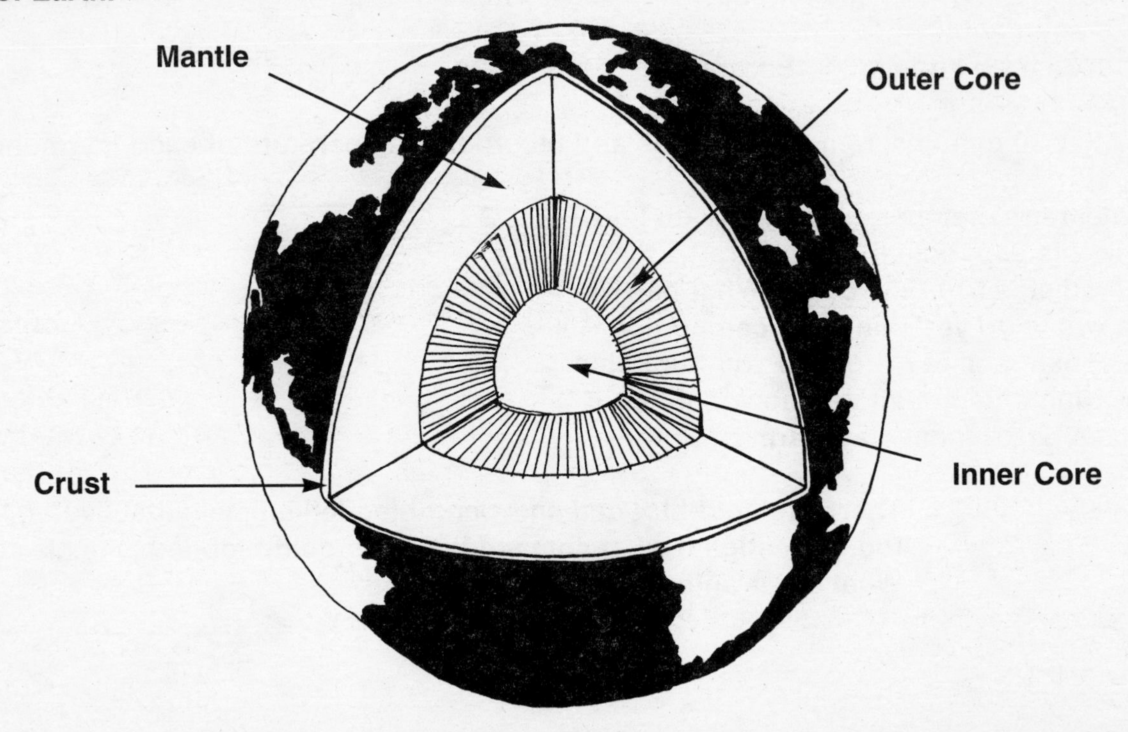

Make A Model Of Earth

What you need:

4 different colors of modeling clay

What to do:

1. Use yellow clay to form the inner core. Yellow is good because it signifies heat. The core is made up mainly of extremely hot iron and nickel.

2. Use orange clay for the outer core. The outer core is molten liquid iron and nickel and some other substances like sulfur.

3. Use red or brown clay for the mantle. It is molten materials in the mantle called magma that flows out through volcanoes.

4. Use green or blue clay to form the crust. Make one volcano by forming a small lump in the crust. Show the movement of magma from the mantle through your volcano.

The deepest hole drilled into the Earth was only 7 miles deep. To get to the center of the Earth it would be necessary to drill about 3,940 more miles. So most of what we know about the Earth results from studying earthquakes and the movement of their vibrations through the Earth. Geologists also study the action of volcanoes to gain more information about the Earth.

What do you think a volcano could tell you about the Earth? ____________________

____

Hot Liquid Rocks Move

There are many "hot spots" in the Earth's mantle. These hot spots are so hot and have so much movement that volcanoes form above them. Pressure builds in the developing or developed volcano until it explodes like the pressure in a shaken soda can. Molten magma in the mantle moves upwards to the crust. Wait a second, did you notice a new word slip in? What is magma? Well, it's the molten rock material beneath Earth's crust.

Lava from volcanoes is magma that has reached Earth's surface. The hot spots heat the magma so hot that the molten rock moves to the surface. Let's see if we can simulate how the movement of magma is affected by heat. We'll use margarine instead of molten rock.

Magma Movement

What you need:

- teaspoon
- soft margarine
- small jar
- a bowl larger than the jar
- warm water
- timer

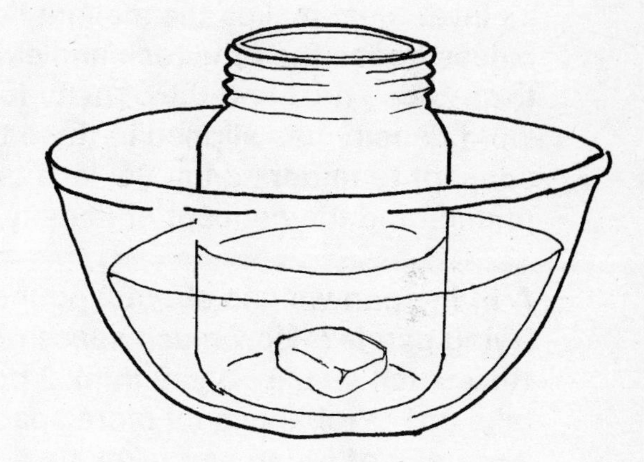

What to do:

1. Put a teaspoon of the soft margarine into the jar. Make sure the margarine is on the bottom of the jar.

2. Turn the jar on its side and describe any movement of the margarine.

3. Half-fill the bowl with warm to hot tap water.

4. Place the jar in the bowl.

5. Let the jar sit in the bowl for at least 4 minutes.

6. Pick the jar up and again observe the movement of the margarine.

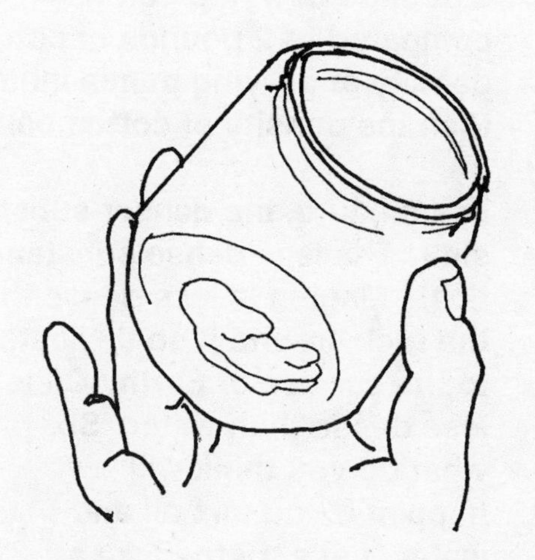

Describe in writing what you observe. Heat increases the energy in molecules. Warm molecules move more than cold molecules.

More Magma Movement

The density of magma affects its movement, too. Magma flows out of volcanoes as lava. Heat makes the magma flow upward but so does its density. Magma is less dense than the rock and earth surrounding it. The combination of the intense heat and the density force the magma to the surface. Okay, the word density has slipped in three times already. And that is a very difficult concept to understand. So, let's take a minute to try to help you understand the concept of density.

A frying pan weighs about 2 pounds. Do you know how big a frying pan is? How much space does a frying pan take up? How much space do you think 2 pounds of cotton balls would take up? Probably a lot more space than a frying pan, huh? 2 pounds of frying pan takes up a little amount of space compared to 2 pounds of cotton balls. So the density of a frying pan is much greater than the density of cotton balls.

In a mixture, the denser substances sink. The less dense substances float. Magma is less dense than the rock around it so it "floats" to the surface of Earth. Oil is less dense than water. So, what do you think will happen if you mix oil and water. Let's try to make a model that shows the effect of density.

Oil And Water

What you need:

timer
spoon
red food coloring
cooking oil
a jar with a lid
water

What to do:

1. Half-fill the jar with water.

2. Stir in food coloring enough to turn the water red.

3. Pour oil into the jar slowly. Pour in a little less oil than water.

4. Tighten the lid. Turn the jar upside down and back again. Describe what happens.

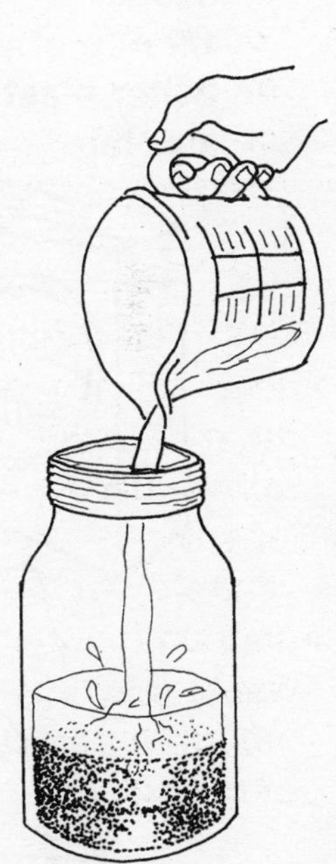

Record the movement of the water and oil. Which substance floats up? Which sinks to the bottom of the jar? Tell which substance is more dense. How do you know?

As you read before, magma is less dense than the rock surrounding it. So it rises to the Earth's surface. Now, compare the ingredients in your experimental mixture to magma and rocks. Which do you think magma is more like, the water or the oil? Which do you think rocks are more like, the water or the oil?

A Plugged Volcano

Sometimes molten magma flows from volcanoes as hot lava shooting out the top. But sometimes the magma cools and hardens inside the volcano. When that happens pressure builds under the hard magma plug. Eventually the pressure blows the magma plug out and causes a violent eruption like the one that took place at Mount St. Helens in Washington State. Try to simulate that kind of eruption.

Blow The Top Off A Volcano

What you need:

a teaspoon of baking soda
tissue
1/2 cup of white vinegar
2-liter plastic soda bottle
a potato

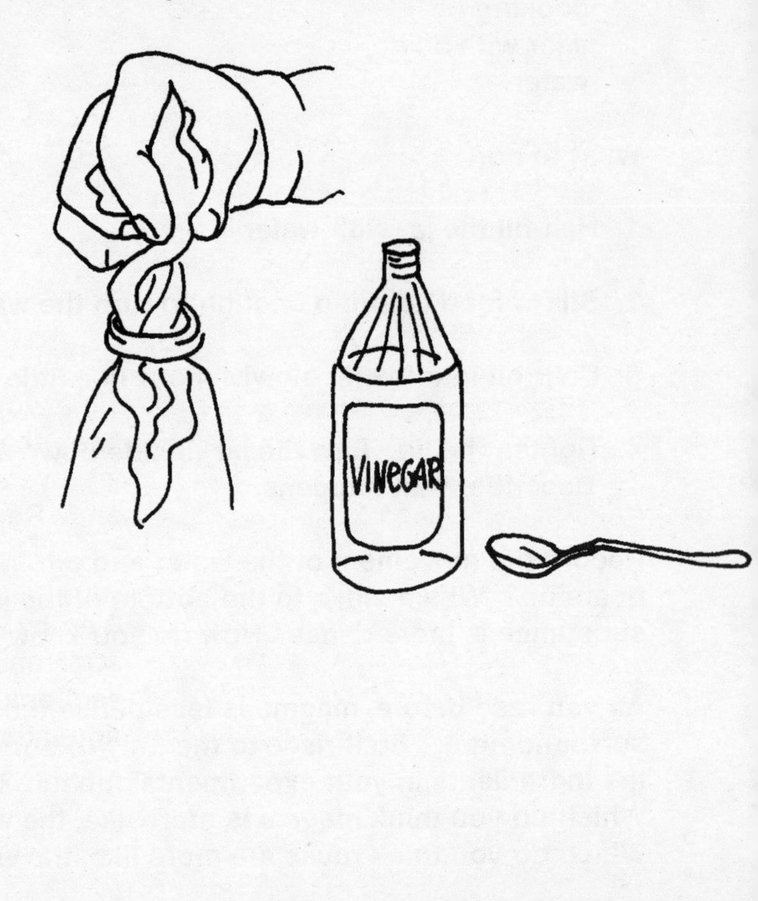

What to do:

1. Ask an adult helper to cut an inch cube of potato. The cube should be large enough to cover the mouth of the bottle.

2. Press the cube over the mouth of the soda bottle. Make at least a 1/4-inch indentation into the potato plug.

3. Do the rest of the experiment outside with your adult helper. Pour the vinegar into the bottle. Place the bottle on a picnic table or on a cement walk.

4. Cut a 3-inch strip of tissue. Put a teaspoon of baking soda on the tissue. Roll the baking soda up in the tissue and twist the ends.

5. Remember, do this next step outside. Drop the packet into the bottle and quickly stop the bottle with the potato cork. Now, stand at least a yard away from the bottle and observe what happens. Record what happened.

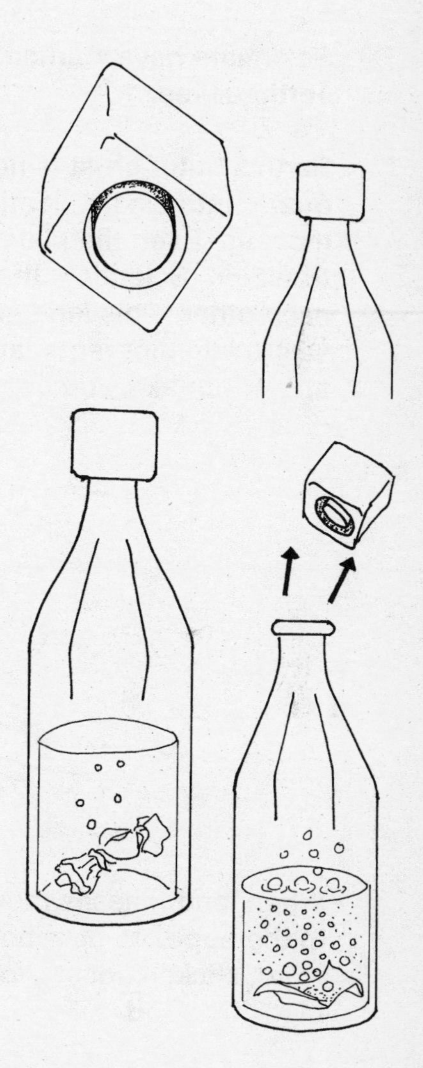

In real volcanoes, the pressure is built up by intense heat not by a chemical reaction of baking soda and vinegar. So don't confuse this reaction with the reactions really taking place in volcanoes. This is simply a simulation.

The Earth's Crust Is Like A Moving Jigsaw Puzzle

Scientists have learned a lot about the make up of the earth by studying volcanoes and earthquakes.

Earth's outer crust is not made up of one single piece. It's cracked like a giant jigsaw puzzle into what scientists call plates. These plates are very slowly but constantly moving. Even the plate on which you live is moving ever so slowly. Some plates push together. Scientists theorize that's how mountain ranges form. Other plates slide past each other. This kind of movement of plates takes place at fault lines. A fault line is where two different plates meet and slide past each other. The next time you hear about an earthquake, you can really say, "That wasn't my fault."

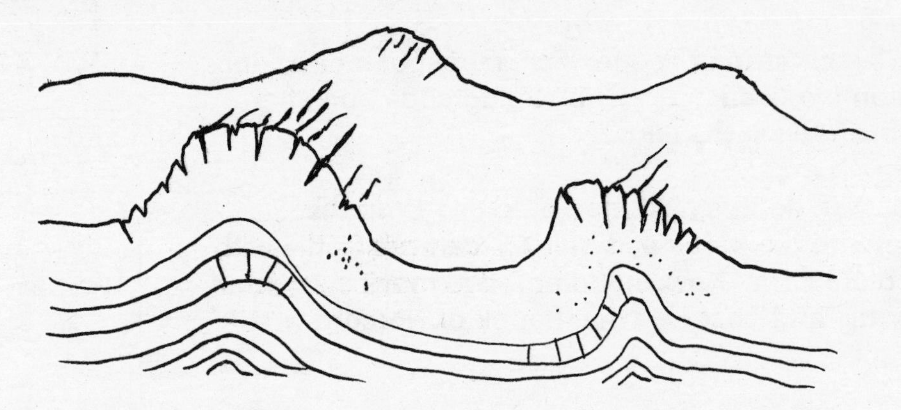

When land masses move at fault lines, one side moves one way and the other side moves in the opposite direction. The surfaces of each are called slickensides. Isn't that a great word, slickensides? You can simulate a slickenside with a piece of sand paper and a block of wood.

Making A Slickenside

What you need:

a block of wood
a piece of very course sandpaper

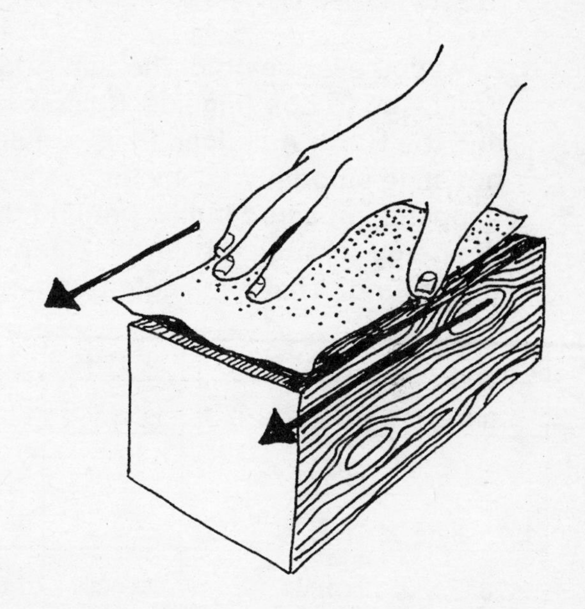

What to do:

1. Sand the block of wood in one direction about 100 times. Make sure you are moving only in one direction.

2. When you have finished, stroke the wood first in the direction you sandpapered. Then stroke the wood in the opposite direction. Be careful of splinters! Compare the directions.

The interesting fact is that scientists can rub their hands along real slickensides and determine in which direction the land is moving. How could you tell which way the sandpaper was moving on your block of wood?

Earthquakes

Have you ever heard of the San Andreas Fault? That is a 300-mile-long fault from San Francisco to Los Angeles, California. The San Andreas Fault is where the Pacific Plate and the North American Plate are sliding past each other. But the edges of the plates do not slide smoothly. Sometimes they wedge against each other and get stuck. When this happens, pressure builds until it forces the two plates to slip. The slipping sends waves of energy through the earth. When the wave of energy hits the surface it usually shakes the ground. That shaking ground is what we call an earthquake.

DATE	PLACE	DEATHS	STRENGTH	DATE	PLACE	DEATHS	STRENGTH
1976 Feb. 4	Guatemala	22,778	7.5	1980 Nov. 23	Italy	4,800	7.2
1976 May 6	Italy	946	6.5	1982 Dec. 13	North Yemen	2,800	6.0
1976 June 26	New Guinea	443	7.1	1983 May 26	Japan	81	7.7
1976 July 28	China	242,000	8.2	1983 Oct. 30	Turkey	1,300	7.1
1976 Aug. 17	Philippines	8,000	7.8	1985 Mar. 3	Chile	146	7.8
1976 Nov. 24	Turkey	4,000	7.9	1985 Sept. 19	Mexico City	4,200+	8.1
1977 Mar. 4	Romania	1,541	7.5	1987 Mar. 5-6	Ecuador	4,000+	7.3
1977 Aug. 19	Indonesia	200	8.0	1988 Aug. 20	Nepal	1,000+	6.5
1977 Nov. 23	Argentina	100	8.2	1988 Nov. 6	China/Burma	1,000	7.3
1978 June 12	Japan	21	7.5	1988 Dec. 7	Armenia	55,000+	6.8
1978 Sept. 16	Iran	25,000	7.7	1989 Oct. 17	San Francisco	62	6.9
1979 Sept. 12	Indonesia	100	8.1	1990 May 30	Peru	115	6.3
1979 Dec. 12	Columbia	800	7.9	1990 June 21	Iran	40,000+	7.7
1980 Oct. 10	Algeria	4,500	7.3	1995 Jan. 17	Kobe, Japan	5,500	7.2

Simulate Plates Sliding Past Each Other

What you need:

two pieces of cloth or plastic wrap
dirt and/or sand
a cake pan
toy cars, trucks, houses or any small objects

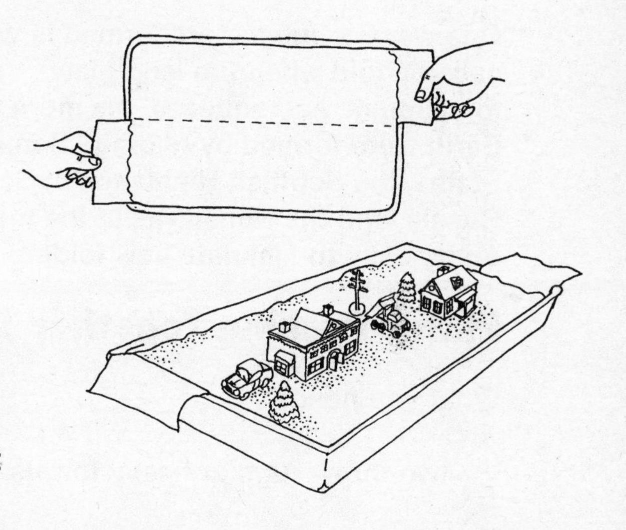

What to do:

1. Lay two pieces of cloth or plastic wrap in the bottom of the cake pan. Make sure you have a lip of cloth or plastic wrap to grab at each end of the pan.

2. Cover the strips of cloth or wrap with dirt or sand. Moisten the dirt or sand slightly.

3. Place the toy cars, houses, trees, or whatever small objects you have down the center of the pan on top of the moist soil.

4. Grasp each lip of the cloth or wrap and pull each strip in the opposite direction.

Describe what happened. Tell how this demonstration is like two plates sliding past each other quickly. Tell how it is different.

Earthquakes are measured on the Richter scale. Very bad earthquakes measure 6 or more on the Richter scale. On July 28 in 1976, 242,000 people were killed in China by an earthquake that registered 8.2 on the Richter scale. The tool scientists use to determine the Richter scale measurement is called a seismometer. Try to find out how they work. How could you find out?

Mountains Grow

One way mountains are formed is when two plates press against each other. This is called a fold when the land plates crush against ocean plates. The more the two plates force, push, and squeeze, the more the mountain grows. Most of the mountain ranges on Earth were formed by folding. Some examples are the Rockies in the Western United States, the Scottish Highlands in Scotland, the Andes in South America, the Urals in Russia, and the Himalayas in the middle and far East. These are only a few examples. It's pretty easy to simulate how folding forms mountains and makes them grow.

Plates Pushing Together To Make A Mountain

What you need:

two throw rugs or heavy towels

What to do:

1. Lay the rugs or towels end to end on the floor.
2. Start pushing them from opposite ends toward each other.

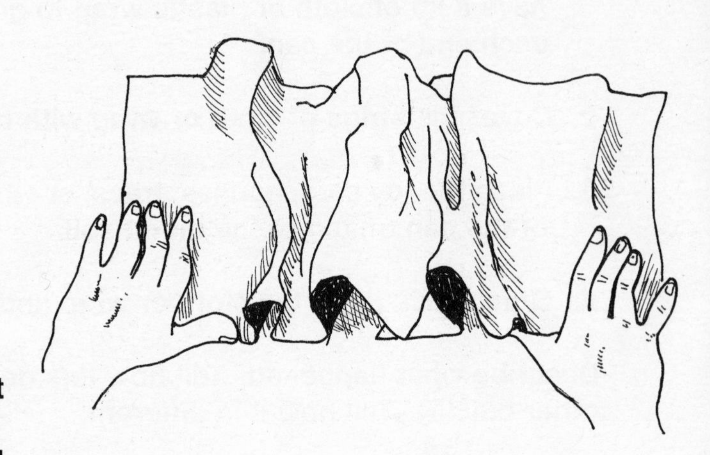

Describe in writing and in drawings what happens as you push the rugs or towels together. Try to compare what happened to the rugs or towels to what happens when two land plates push together.

Light, Heat, Electricity

"Mike, quick turn on the TV!"

"Hurry up, kids, dinner's ready."

"Can I use your flashlight to find my dime?"

"RRNNNGGG, rise and shine!"

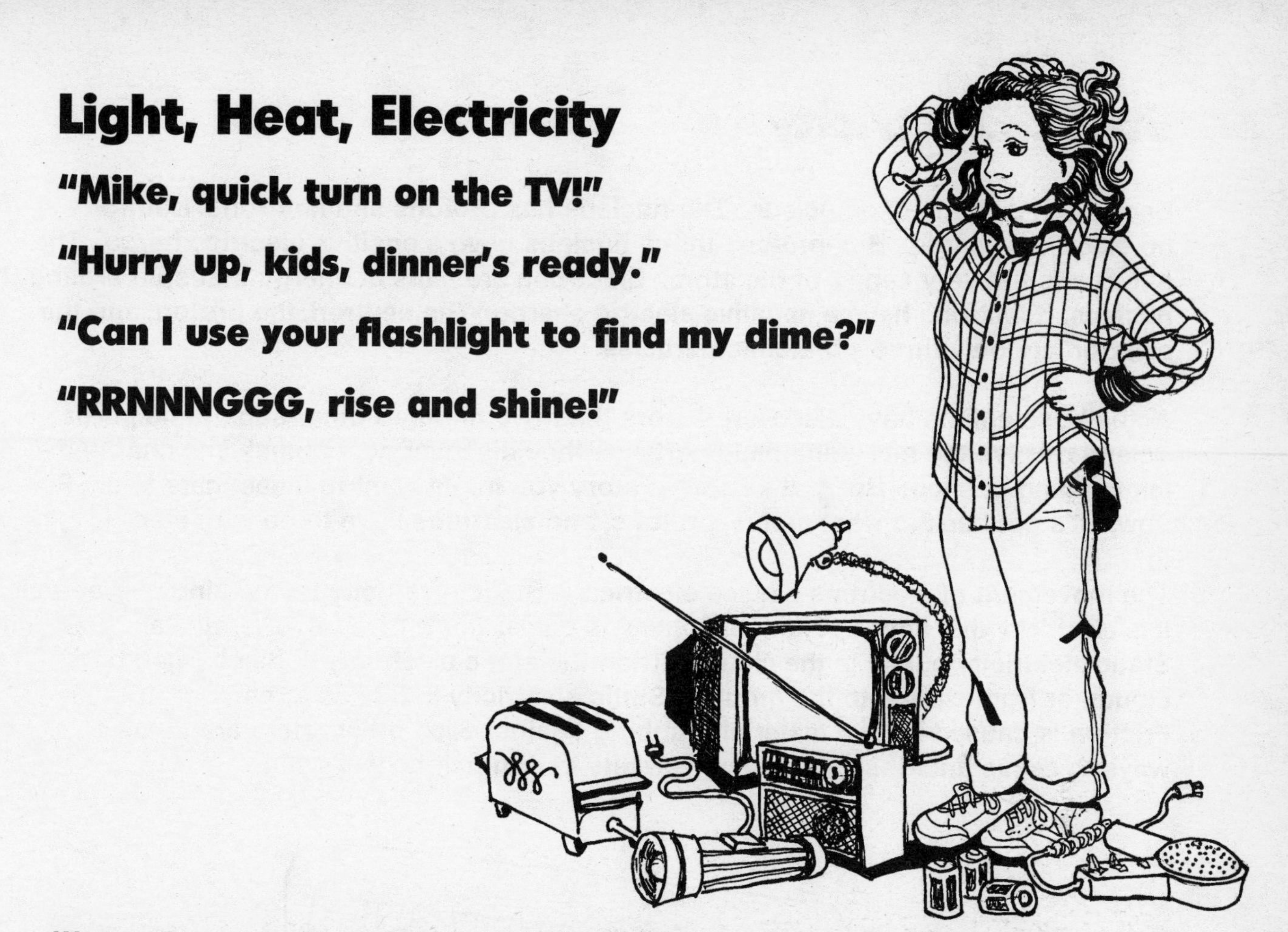

We turn it on, heat it up, light it, and plug it in–all thanks to electrical energy. People have become dependent on electricity.

How does matter become electrically charged? Remember that cells are the building blocks of all living things. Well, atoms are the smallest building blocks of everything you see around you. Matter is anything that takes up space and has mass, such as gases, liquids, and solids. Everything you see, hear, feel, smell, and taste is made up of atoms. It would take millions of atoms just to cover the period that ends this sentence.

Static Electricity

Each atom is made of a nucleus. The nucleus has protons and neutrons. Neutrons have no electrical charge. But, protons in the nucleus have a positive electric charge. The nucleus is the very center of the atom. Electrons are balls of energy that spin around the nucleus. Electrons have a negative electric charge. The neutron, the proton, and the electron are only three subatomic particles.

Actually, scientists have discovered more than two hundred other subatomic particles. Scientists give the new subatomic particles they discover neat names like charmed lambda and upsilon. But that's another story you might want to investigate later. For now, let's get back to what atoms, protons, and electrons have to do with electricity.

The movement of electrons causes electricity. Static electricity is one kind of electricity. It is electricity that does not flow. Lightning is one example of very powerful static electricity. Static electricity builds in the clouds. Then the static electricity is discharged between clouds or from clouds to the ground. Static electricity builds as a result of friction. Friction is caused by two materials rubbing against each other. Here are some easy ways to cause and observe static electricity in non painful ways.

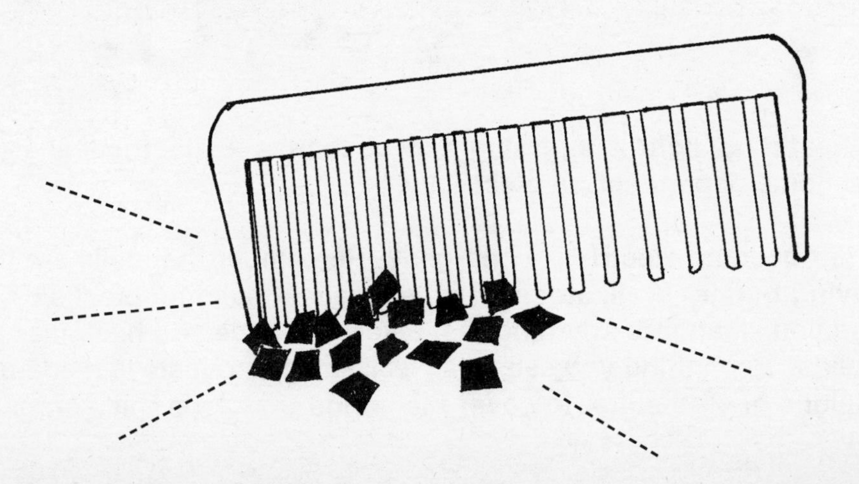

Safe Static Electricity

What you need:

a balloon
ruler
tissue paper
scissors
comb

What to do:

1. Cut tiny confetti from the tissue. Cut the confetti about 1/8 to 1/4-inch squares. A hole punch works well to make confetti.
2. Place the confetti on a table.
3. Run the comb through your hair quickly several times.
4. Hold the teeth of the comb near the confetti. Describe what happens. The negative electrons on the comb attract the positive part of the atoms in the paper.
5. Blow up your balloon and rub it against your hair several times quickly. Now place the balloon on the wall. Describe what happens. How was your balloon like your comb, besides using them to rub against your hair?

   Describe some other times when you observed or experienced the result of static electricity.

   ____

   ____

Getting A Charge From A Lemon

Getting electricity from a comb or a balloon is neat. But you can get electricity from some other real interesting things, too. You can make a very weak battery from a lemon. A battery really only needs two kinds of metal and an acid to make electricity. A car battery has sulfuric acid which is a very powerful and dangerous acid. A lemon has citric acid which is not real powerful and is not dangerous.

Make A Lemon Battery

What you need:

a paper clip
a lemon
a piece of copper wire or a penny
a flashlight light bulb

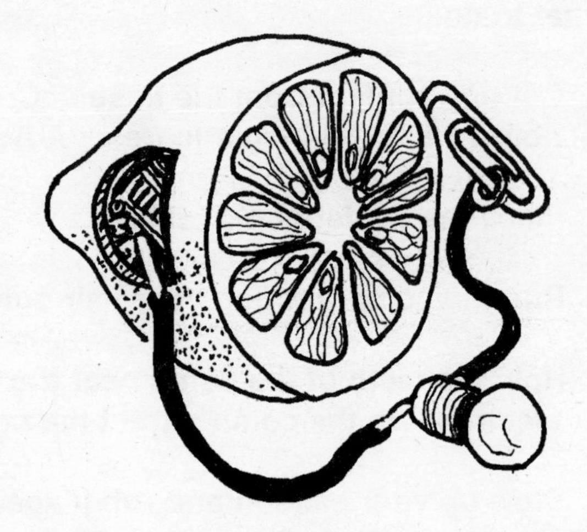

What to do:

1. Make sure there is no insulation on the ends of the copper wire. Put one end of the copper wire into the lemon. Make sure it goes through the skin to the fruity part.

2. Straighten a paper clip. Put one end of the paper clip into the lemon. Make sure it goes into the fruity part.

3. Hold the ends of the paper clip and the copper wire sticking out of the lemon. Touch the metal end of the flashlight light bulb with both wires (or the paper clip and the penny) at the same time.

Describe what happened. You may have to look very closely at the bulb. A lemon makes a very weak battery. If you touch your tongue to the two wires, you will probably feel a very tiny tingle. The water on your tongue makes a good conductor. Remember, this was a lemon. NEVER touch other bare wires.

Try to think of another way you can get energy from a lemon. This other kind of energy is the same kind of energy you can get from a banana, a glass of milk, and a peanut butter sandwich.

____

____

____

____

____

Energy Works For Us

The reason we need energy is to do work for us. So scientists have worked hard to find ways of capturing energy and making it useful. A steam turbine is one way of changing energy from one form into another more usable form of energy. In a steam turbine, fuel is burned to boil water. The water changes to steam when it boils. Usually the steam would take up more space than the liquid water, but in the case of the steam turbine it is confined to a small space. Pressure builds up. When the pressure has built to a high enough pressure level, the steam is released through a small opening. When the escaping steam is directed at fan blades, the blades turn. You can make a steam turbine fan with an adult helper's assistance.

A Turbine Fan

What you need:

- an aluminum pie pans
- paper fan on next page
- scissors
- a ball-point pen cap
- tape
- modeling clay
- a large paper clip
- radiator or heating vent
- a clay flower pot or any tall pot
- an adult helper

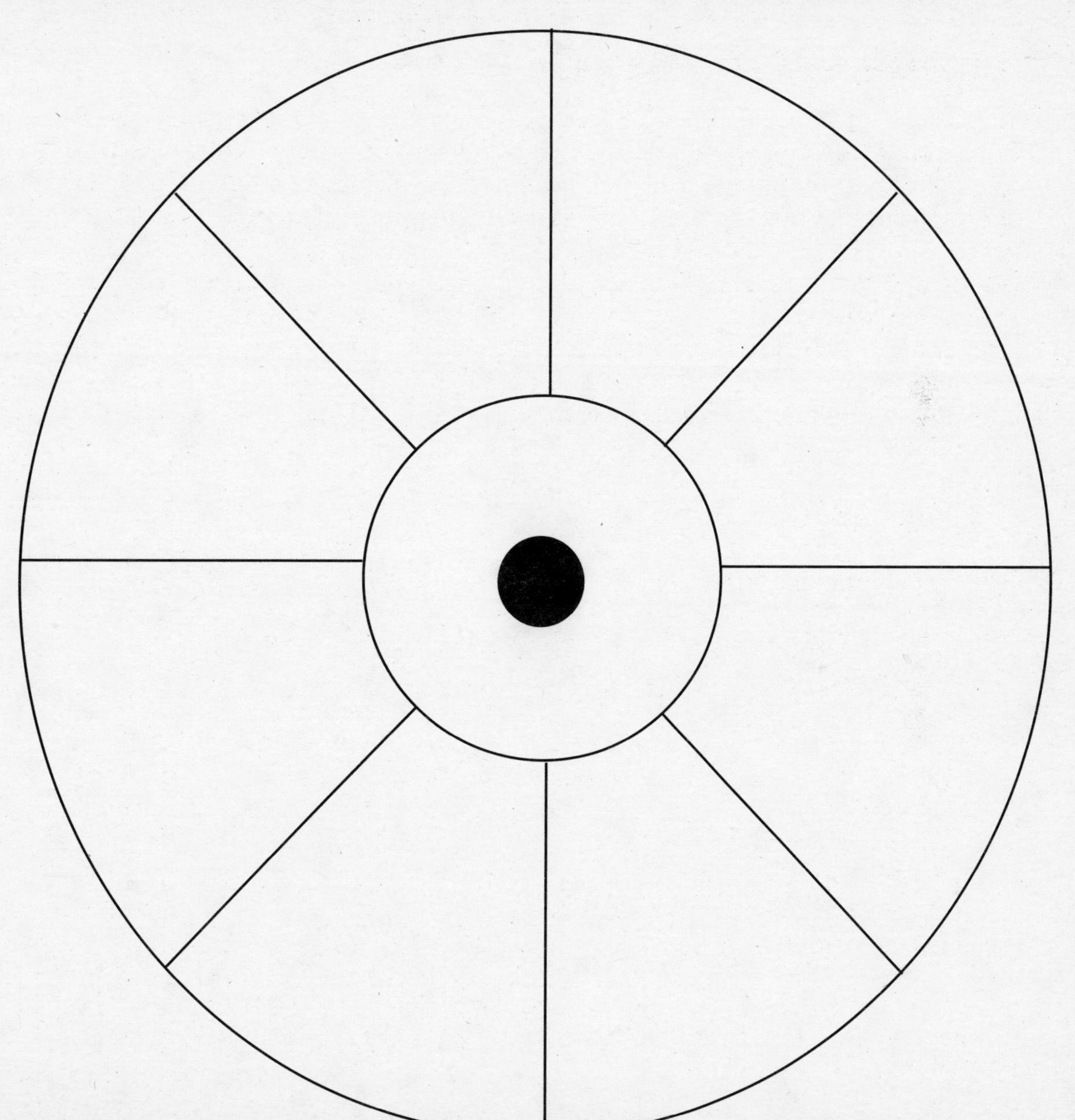

What to do:

CAUTION: a radiator or heating vent can get hot enough to burn. Ask your adult helper to set up the fan.

1. Cut out the fan guide on page 71.

2. Use the guide to cut a circle out of the bottom of one foil pie pan. Make a very small hole in the center of the foil.

3. Tape the fan guide to the aluminum foil and cut the foil along the lines marked.

4. Bend each section of the foil fan.

5. Push the pen cap through the center hole and tape the pen cap in place.

6. Turn the flower pot upside down. Put a small lump of clay in the center of the bottom of the flower pot. Ask your adult helper to set the flower pot on the radiator, over, or near a heating vent.

7. Straighten out the large paper clip and stand it up in the clay.

8. Place your turbine over the paper clip.

9. Watch what happens as the heat from the radiator or the heating vent hits the fan blades.

Observe what happens. Draw a picture of your fan.

What happens to the fan when the heat hits the blades?

____

Which way do the blades move?

____

Describe in your own words how a steam turbine works. What simulates the steam in this experiment?

____

____

The Flow Of Electricity

Most electricity comes to our homes through wires. Electricity flows through wires at different rates. We can see current electricity at work almost everywhere—light bulbs change electricity to light, heaters into heat, motors to motion. Electricity is an easy energy to use because we can make it flow. Most electric currents are a stream of electrons. And the rate it flows through wires can be measured. The amount of current is called amperes or amps. This activity shows how to measure the flow rate of salt. The flow rate of salt simulates the flow rate of electricity. It is not an exact model, but it does show how the size of a wire can affect the flow rate of electricity.

The Size Of Wires Affects The Flow Of Electricity

What you need:

- a pencil
- a paper cup that can hold 6 ounces of salt
- masking tape
- 6 ounces of salt
- a bowl
- stopwatch
- a helper

What to do:

1. Punch a hole in the bottom of the paper cup with a pencil. The hole should be about as big around as the pencil.

2. Place a piece of masking tape on the outside bottom of the cup. Make sure the tape covers the hole.

3. Fill the cup with salt.

4. Hold the cup over the bowl and get ready to remove the masking tape.

5. Ask your helper to start the stopwatch when you remove the masking tape.

6. Ask your helper to stop the watch the second the salt stops pouring out the hole.

The flow rate of the salt is equal to the amount of salt pouring out, ounces, divided by the amount of time it took the salt to pour out of the cup, seconds.

The size of the hole will affect the rate of flow just like the size of wire affects the flow of electricity. Try the experiment with a larger hole; a smaller hole. Record your results.

Find some different types of electrical appliances in your home. Compare the size of the wires that power the appliance. Notice those wires with three-pronged plugs. How does the diameter of a wire with a three-pronged plug compare to the diameter of a wire with a two-pronged plug? What does that comparison tell you about the appliances? Remember, you must have three-holed outlets to use a three-pronged plug!

Circuits

A flashlight is a good example of a circuit. Switch on a flashlight and you have just completed a circuit. The electricity in a battery flows from the battery through the switch to the light bulb and back to the battery. This is called a circuit. In most flashlights, the circuit is called a series circuit. A series circuit has only one path the electric current can follow.

Here are symbols to use for drawing circuits.

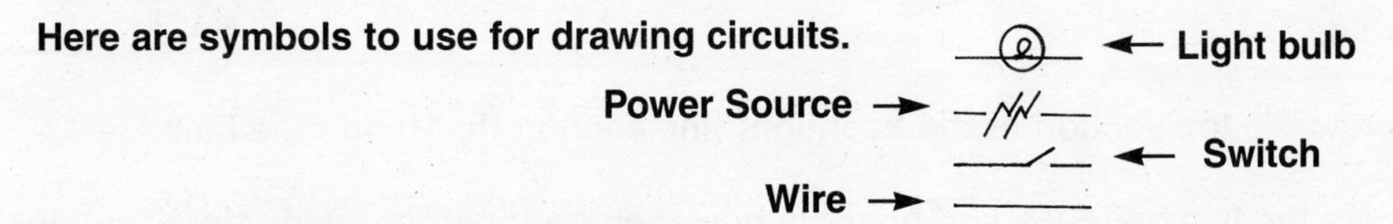

Here is the diagram of a series circuit with one battery, one wire, one switch, and one light bulb. This is how the series circuits in most flashlights would be diagrammed.

Series Circuit

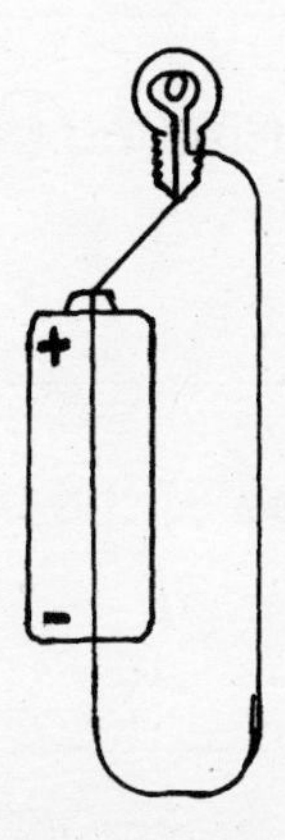

Using these symbols, diagram your own series circuit with two light bulbs, two batteries, and one switch.

A Circuit In A Flashlight

What you need:

a flashlight that holds 2 D sized batteries
a pencil
2 D sized batteries
paper or science journal

What to do:

1. Unscrew the top section of the flashlight (the section that holds the bulb.)

2. Remove the two batteries and observe how they go together inside the flashlight case. What do you think the + and the - indicate on the batteries?

____

3. Look at the bottom and the inside of the case or holder. Do you see a metal spring in the bottom of the flashlight? What do you think the metal spring is for?

____

4. Look carefully at the sides of the case. What do you see running from the bottom of the case to the top of the case?

____

5. Study the flashlight bulb and bulb holder. What is the base of the bulb made of? What do you observe inside the glass part of the bulb?

____

6. Draw the circuit you think is connected when the flashlight is put together correctly.

7. Put your flashlight back together and make sure it works. What do you think the switch does to turn the light on? What do you think the switch does to turn the light off?

____

____

Parallel Circuits

If all of the lights in your home were connected in a series circuit, what do you think would happen if you turned one light off? Electric wiring for most homes is not wired in a series circuit like a flashlight. Most wiring provides more than one path for the current to follow. This kind of circuit is called a parallel circuit.

Parallel Circuit

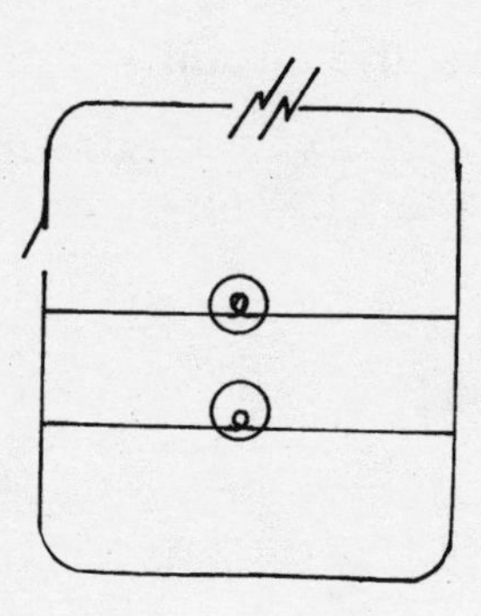

When one light in your home is turned off, it does not usually affect the other lights in your home. Most homes are wired with parallel circuits. Here is one example of a parallel circuit. Remember, this is only a model.

Light bulb

Power Source

Switch

Wire

Parallel Circuit In A Room

Using the symbols for light bulb, energy source, switch, and wire, diagram a parallel circuit of one room showing one energy source, three lamps, and two switches.

Hint: look around the room you are in right now. How many switches do you see? How many lamps do you see?

Electrical Safety

Safety is important around electricity. Here are some situations. Describe what safe action you should take for each.

My two-year-old sister is playing with keys near a socket.

My dad is using an electric drill in the garage. I hear a loud pop and find him on the floor.

My toast is stuck in the toaster.

Electrical Safety Checklist

Here's a checklist you can use to inspect your environment.

Inspection Site ____Home _____School

	Yes	No
1. Are open outlets covered with childproof caps?	____	____
2. Are electrical cords in good condition?	____	____
3. Are extension cords used correctly?	____	____
4. Are electrical cords away from heat sources?	____	____
5. Are electrical cords away from water sources?	____	____
6. Are heat-producing appliances away from flammable materials?	____	____
7. Is anyone trained in CPR?	____	____
8. Does everyone know the correct use of 9-1-1 or other emergency numbers?	____	____
9. Are there smoke alarms on every floor?	____	____
10. Do the batteries work?	____	____

A Power Plant

Electricity is produced for our use from several sources of energy – the wind – nuclear energy – the movement of water. But, about 70 percent of the electricity in our country is produced by power plants that burn fossil fuels. Fossil fuels are coal, natural gas, and petroleum. They are used to produce heat and electricity, and to operate machines like cars, lawn mowers, planes, and trucks.

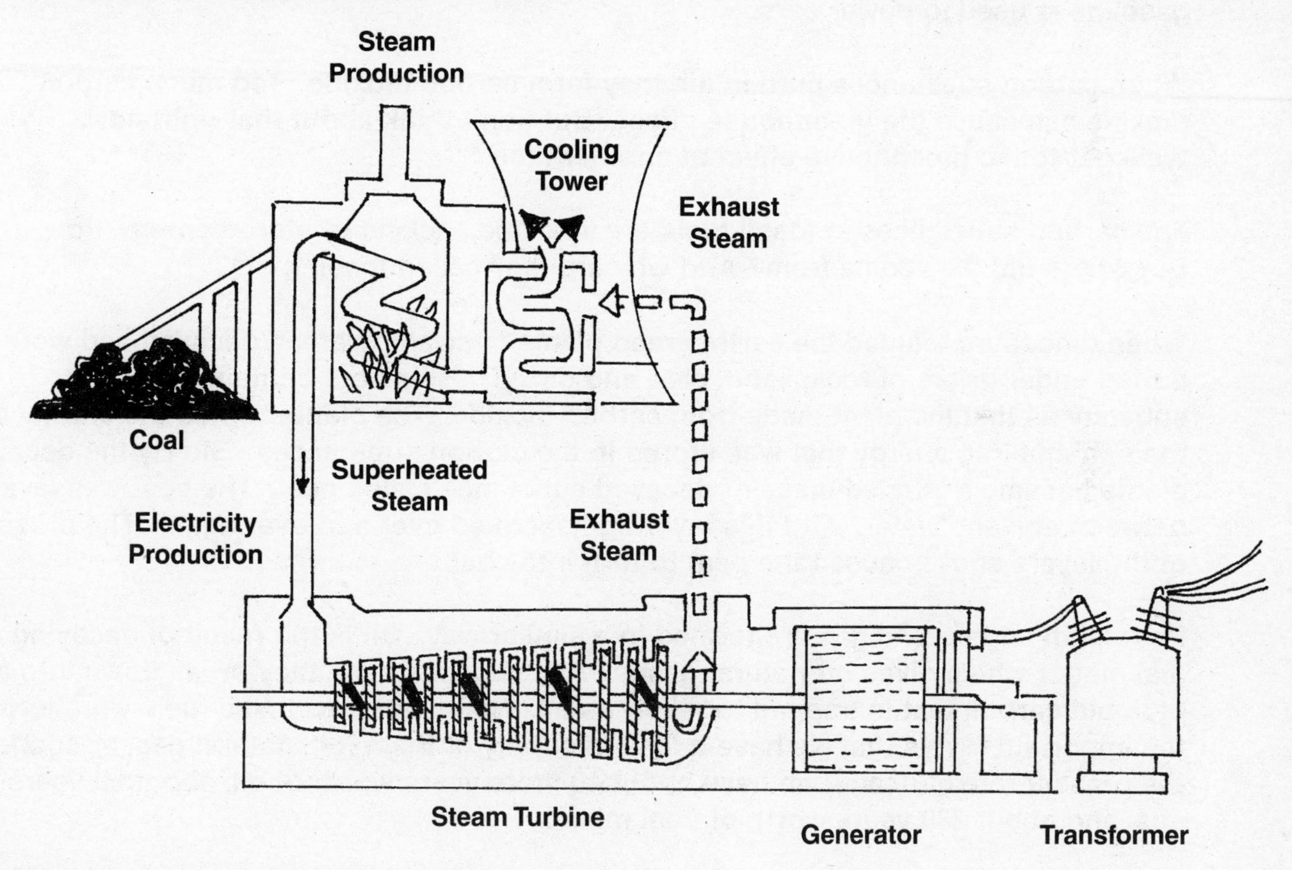

Fossil Fuels

The fossil fuels that are used to run machines and produce electricity contain carbon substances. Carbon is a very important element. No living thing could survive without carbon. In nature carbon occurs by itself in diamonds and something called graphite. When it mixes with other substances, carbon occurs in fossil fuels such as coal. Carbon also occurs in the air as carbon dioxide. Carbon monoxide is the gas given off when gasoline is used to power cars.

When carbon substances burn in air, they form carbon dioxide. Too much carbon dioxide can cause the greenhouse effect. But don't think about that right now. We'll get to the greenhouse effect at another time.

The carbon substances in fossil fuels are like little packets of stored energy, now. But where did they come from? And why are they called fossil fuels?

When dinosaurs roamed the earth, green plants in swampy areas decayed and were buried under layers of rock, sand, clay, and dirt. These plants contained carbon substances that the plant made from carbon dioxide. The plants turned the energy in the sunlight into energy that was stored in the carbon substances. Slowly the decaying plants became a tangled mass of decayed substance called peat. The peat was layered between soil and water. And this layering happened over and over again. The pressure of the layers above caused the peat to turn into coal.

Petroleum and natural gas are formed in a similar way. Oil is the result of decaying animal matter which gives off natural gases. As the gases heat, they break down into a kind of liquid carbon that is trapped together as oil. No matter how fossil fuels were formed, the important fact is that we have a limited supply of them (oil, natural gas, or coal). At the present rate of usage, we have about 40 more years worth of oil, about 60 years of gas, and about 250 years worth of coal mined.

Drilling For Oil

Today, oil companies mine for fossil fuels such as coal and drill for other fossil fuels such as oil and natural gas. This activity will show you two things about fossil fuels. First, how difficult it is to retrieve from the earth and second how difficult it is to clean up if it is spilled accidentally.

A Simulated Oil Pump

What you need:

hot water
a plastic bottle with spray pump (clear works best)
cold water
pebbles or marbles
plastic tubing (about a foot to fit the pump nozzle)
motor oil or cooking oil colored with blue food coloring
three jars the same size
masking tape
a bowl

What to do:

1. Half-fill the clear plastic spray bottle with pebbles (marbles).
2. Half-fill one jar with motor oil and mark the top level with masking tape.
3. Pour the jar of motor oil over the pebbles (marbles).
4. Fasten the spray pump to the bottle.
5. Attach the plastic tubing to the spray nozzle.
6. Place the other end of the tubing in the bowl or the oil jar you just emptied.
7. Pump the spray pump to get the oil out of the bottle.
8. Half-fill a second jar with cold water.
9. Pour the cold water into the spray bottle. Place the end of the tubing in the cold water jar you just emptied and pump.
10. Half-fill the third jar with warm to hot water. Pour the warm water into the spray bottle and pump again.

How much oil did you get out from your first pumping?

___

How much oil did you get out from your second pumping?

___

How much oil did you get out from your third pumping?

___

How much oil was left in the bottle after you pumped out the warm water?

___

How do you think this simulation is like an oil well?

___

___

How do you think this simulation shows that it is difficult to clean up all the oil after an oil spill?

___

___

Investigate what it takes to clean up an accidental oil spill in nature. Design some of your own ideas on how oil spills could be cleaned. Write some ideas about how accidental oil spills can be avoided in the first place.

Make Your Own Fossil Network Tree

Once companies have retrieved the oil, called petroleum, they have to refine it to use it. Petroleum directly from the wells is separated into thin and thick oils. Thick oils can be used as lubricants, such as the heavy grease that lubricates an airplane's landing gear or a car's gears. The thin oils are refined to make gasoline, jet fuel, home heating oil, and other types of fuels. When certain chemicals are added to oil, other types of petrochemicals are formed. These petrochemicals are used to manufacture products such as soap, perfume, medicine, fertilizers, synthetic fiber, plastic, and rubber.

Make a network tree and list some of the different products you know of that fall under each category.

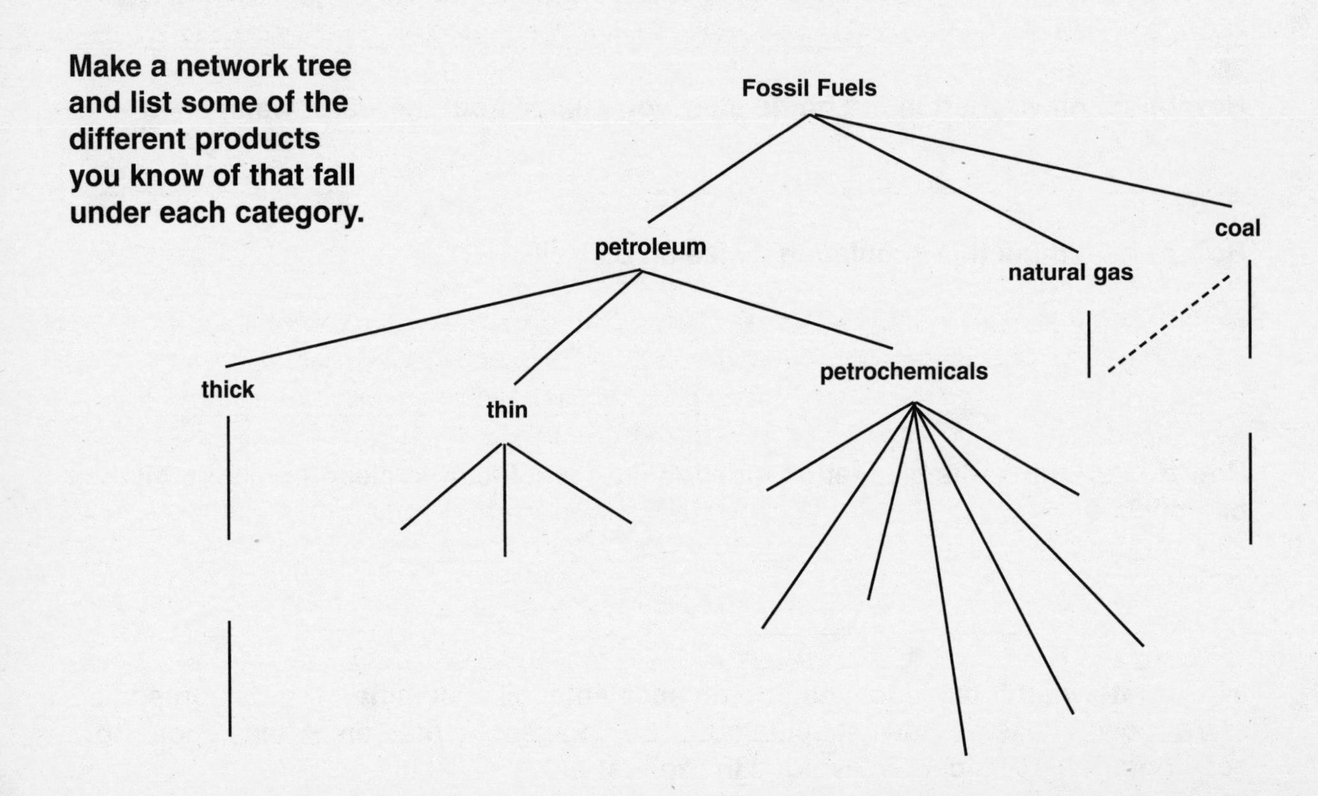

The Greenhouse Effect

The use of fossil fuels is both good and bad. Using fossil fuels produces electricity, heat, light, and makes our lives more comfortable. But the more fuels we use, the less there are for the future. And using fossil fuels creates different kinds of problems for us. Burning fossil fuels causes air pollution and the greenhouse effect. And using synthetic substances like plastic and fertilizers causes some of the solid and water pollution in our world today.

Remember, we mentioned the greenhouse effect before. What is the greenhouse effect? Tell what you already know about greenhouses or about the greenhouse effect.

____

____

____

The Earth is like a giant greenhouse. The air surrounding the Earth is like the glass or plastic windows around a greenhouse. The air surrounding the earth is called the atmosphere. It is made up of gases, water vapor, dust, and dirt. Oxygen and nitrogen are gases that make up most of the atmosphere we breathe. But other gases, sometimes called greenhouse gases, are also in the atmosphere. Some of these greenhouse gases are made by people. The greenhouse gases act like the glass in a greenhouse and trap heat on Earth. What if there were too much of the greenhouse gases? Do you think Earth could get too hot?

____

____

____

The Greenhouse Effect In A Shoe Box

What you need:

two shoe boxes
two thermometers
plastic wrap

What to do:

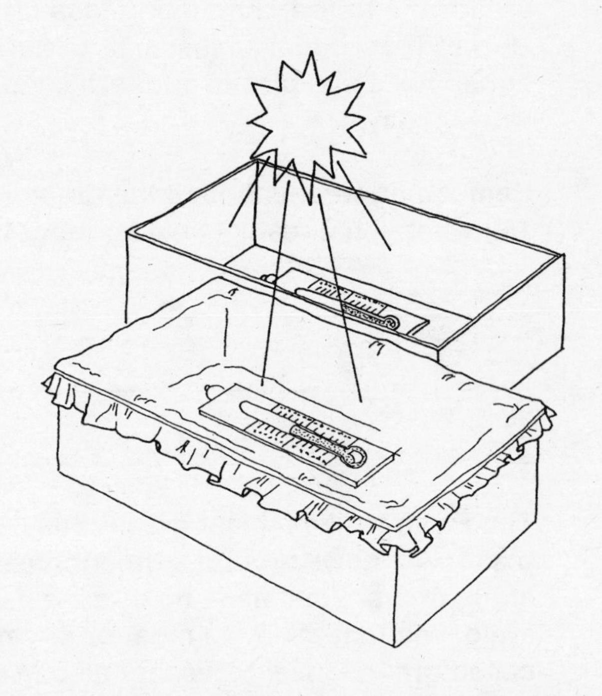

1. Place a thermometer in each shoe box.

2. Cover one shoe box with plastic wrap.

3. Place both boxes in the sunlight. Record the temperature in each box. The temperature in each box should be the same when you start your experiment.

4. After 30 minutes in the sun, measure the temperature in each box again and record the temperature.

Compare the temperatures in each box. Why do you think the temperature in one box was higher than in the other box? How is the box with the plastic wrap like a greenhouse? How do you think what happened in the box with the plastic wrap is like what happens in the greenhouse effect? How could you use what you just learned to start your own greenhouse for growing plants even during the winter? Design a greenhouse of your own.

The Greenhouse Effect Effect

List some possible changes on Earth if the greenhouse effect causes global warming. Write a sentence to explain a possible effect of each change.

Change	Effect
Very cold places on Earth become warmer.	
Warmer temperatures cause more rain, tornadoes, and hurricanes.	
Hot temperatures dry up water in lakes, rivers, ponds, and soil.	

Pollution

Another type of pollution is the accidental spilling of fossil fuel. Fossil fuels like oil are accidentally spilled into the environment too often. You have probably heard of major oil spills. But even small spills pollute the environment. Gasoline spills from mowers or oil leaks from cars are two examples. Look around where you live. Do you see any signs of oil or gasoline pollution? Look for grease stains. Look for multicolored, shiny spots on the surface of water. Record what you see.

Oil and water stay separate but some other pollutants do mix together to create new substances. Some of these new substances can cause real problems. Let's look at how some substances mix together.

An Oil Spill Is A Real Mess

What you need:

sand
baking soda
cooking oil
bowls
small jars with lids
measuring spoons
labels and markers
sugar
water
vinegar

What to do:

1. Half-fill one jar with water. Add a tablespoon of oil. Close the lid and shake the jar. Record what happens. Try to remove the oil from the water. In writing, explain how you tried. Compare your try to an attempt to clean up a giant oil spill in the ocean.

2. Mix some sand into the oil and water in a jar. Let it sit for a few minutes. Describe what happens.

3. Mix some sugar and some sand together in a bowl. Describe what you see.

4. Mix a teaspoon of baking soda into a jar of water. Tighten the lid and shake. Describe what happens.

5. Now add 2 tablespoons of vinegar to the mixture of the jar of oil and water. Describe what happens.

What substances stayed separate in your experiments? ____________________

What are some pollutants in our environment like these substances? ____________

What substances formed solutions with the water? ______________________

Solutions do not produce new substances. They share the characteristics of each of the substances that mixed together. For example, if you mix red paint with white paint, it's still paint but it is pink, somewhere between the two substances.

What are some pollutants in our environment like these substances? ____________

____

What substances mixed together to cause a chemical reaction? Here's a hint, the bubbles formed by mixing the substances were carbon dioxide bubbles, a new substance.

____

____

Oil Spills Are More Than Messy

What does oil that is accidentally spilled in the environment do to living things? Let's try a little experiment with a feather to try to observe one reason oil harms living creatures. This experiment shows the bad effect oil spills can have on birds.

Oil Spills Can Kill Living Organisms

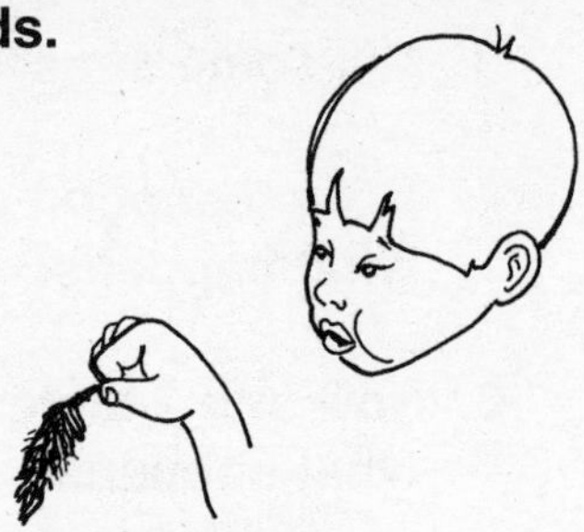

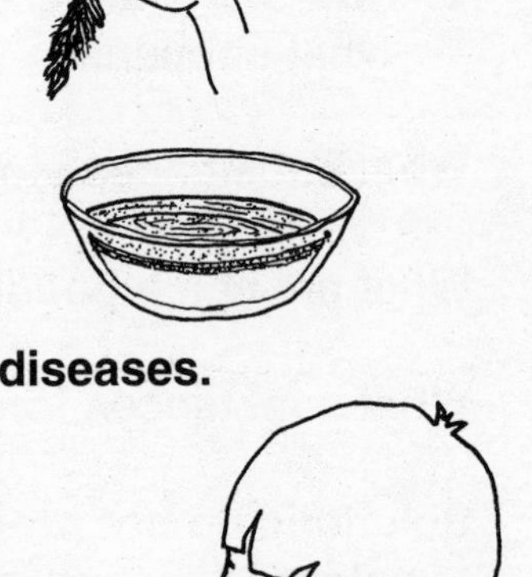

What you need:

a small bowl
tap water
3 tablespoons of cooking oil
two 2 to 3–inch long feathers

Before you begin this experiment, remember:
Do not pick up bird feathers from the ground. They can carry diseases.

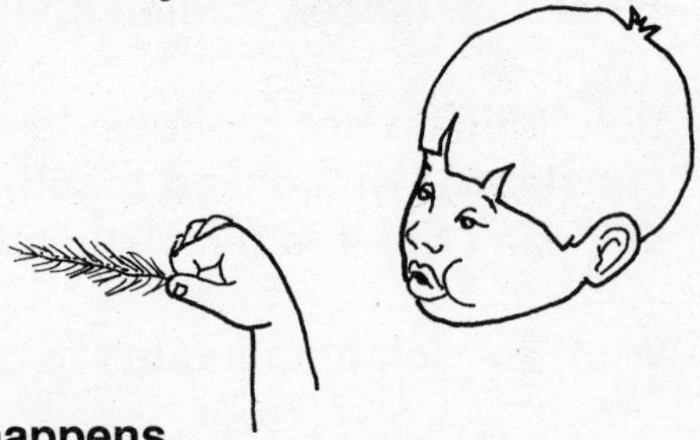

What to do:

1. Half-fill the bowls with water.
2. Gently lay a feather in one of the bowls.
3. Pick up the feather and blow on it. Record what happens. Does the feather dry quickly? Does it move easily from you breath?
4. Pour the cooking oil into the bowl. Now gently lay the second feather in the layer of oil. Pick up the feather and blow on it. Record what happens. Does this feather seem to dry quickly?

How does this experiment show what effect oil can have on birds in the environment? What kinds of effects do you think oil spills could have on other living things?

Nuclear Fission

Nuclear energy is another form of energy. Nuclear energy is the most powerful kind of energy known today. You can get the most amount of energy from the least amount of fuel with nuclear energy.

One way scientists have found to create nuclear energy is by splitting the nucleus of an atom into two parts. Remember, an atom has a nucleus with protons and neutrons. Uranium is the mineral used to create nuclear energy. Uranium does not contain a carbon substance, so pollutants like those released by fossil fuels are not released by nuclear fission.

But, nuclear power plants can release very dangerous substances into the environment accidentally. Did you ever hear about Chernobyl in Russia? Look it up and tell what happened at the nuclear power plant in Chernobyl. Did you ever hear about Three Mile Island near Harrisburg, Pennsylvania?

Research what happened at Three Mile Island and tell about it. There is another reason that nuclear energy is a problem. Radioactive waste that produces dangerous radiation is created as a waste product when a nucleus is divided (nuclear fission). The radioactive waste can be harmful for 1,000 years or even more.

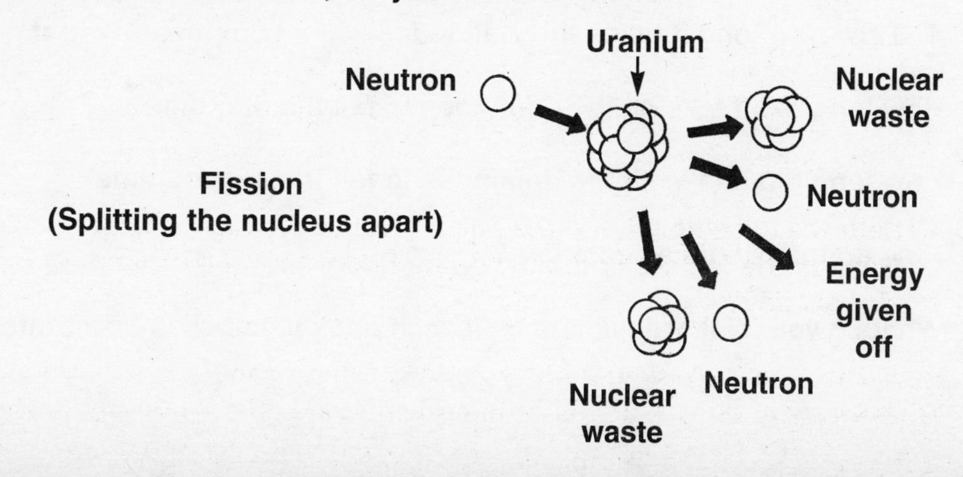

Fission
(Splitting the nucleus apart)

A Chain Reaction

Nuclear energy is produced when nuclei (more than one nucleus) begin separating. A nuclear reaction is a chain reaction that involves billions of atoms. Do you know what a chain reaction is? Let's watch one in action.

The Domino Effect

What you need:

25 or more dominoes a stopwatch

What to do:

1. Stand the dominoes up on their short side about one inch apart in a line.
2. Time how long it takes them all to fall when you push the first one into the second domino.
3. Stand them up again, but this time stand them up so that each domino will knock over two other dominoes.
4. Time how long it takes them all to fall when you push the first.

How long did it take all the dominoes to fall the first time? ____________________

How long did it take all the dominoes to fall the second time? ____________________

How do the two times compare? ____________________

What do you think would happen if each domino knocked down three, four, five dominoes?

____

Nuclear Fusion

Now, the only way to dispose of nuclear waste is to store it in deep tunnels. This is very expensive and could be harmful if the storage containers ever leaked. But there is another kind of nuclear energy scientists are studying. This is called nuclear fusion. This reaction is the opposite of nuclear fission. This reaction happens when two nuclei combine (fuse together) and form a heavier nucleus. This kind of reaction does not form any pollution. And, if scientists can find a way to control fusion reactions, we could have an unlimited supply of safe fuel. The sun has been producing energy by fusion for millions and millions of years. But scientists have not found a practical way to control the energy that is released. Actually it takes more energy now to cause nuclear fusion than is created from nuclear fusion.

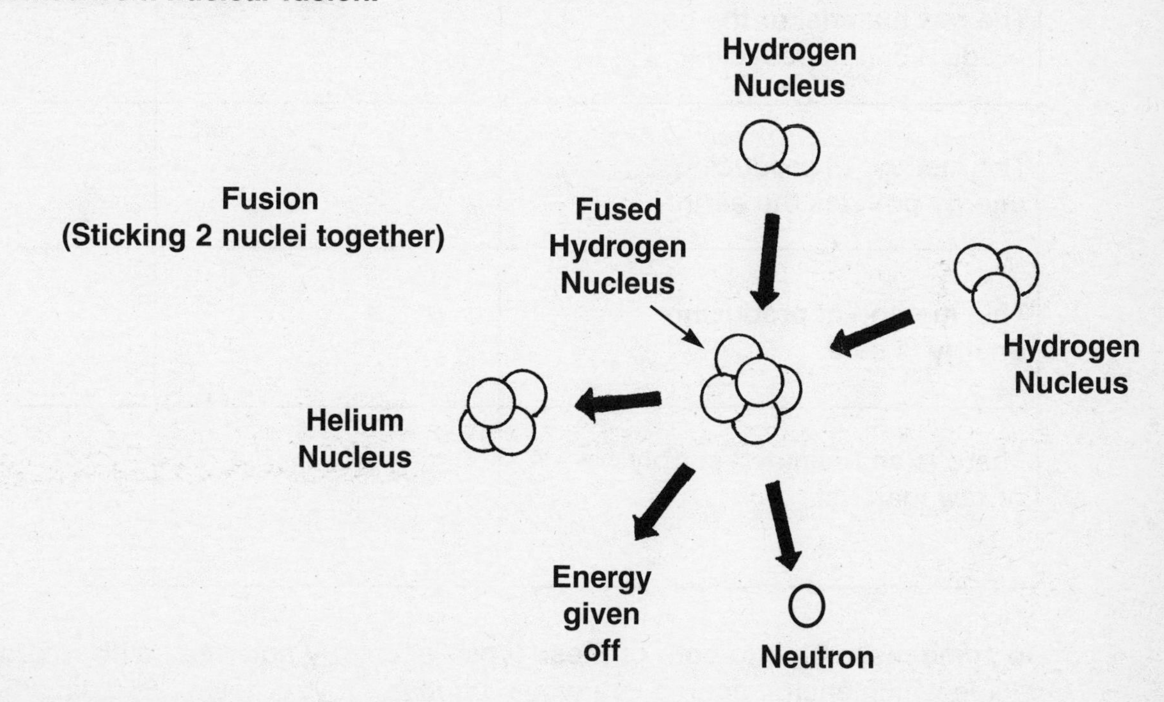

Energy Sources Comparison Matrix

Read the headings for the rows and columns. In each column, fill in the answer that describes the energy source statement. Write a reason for each of your answers.

	Nuclear Fission	Fossil Fuels
What is the raw material needed?		
The raw material or the final product can be recycled.		
The method of producing energy pollutes the earth.		
This method of producing energy is safe.		
There is an unlimited supply of raw material.		

Do some research into both of these types of energy sources. With what you find out, decide which energy source you would choose for your town. Explain why? What other energy sources are possible?

Other Kinds Of Energy Sources

What other energy sources do you think are available? What about the sun? Scientists have been studying solar energy for a long time. And people have been using it for a long time, too. The sun can be used to heat buildings. This is known as passive solar heating. Let's simulate solar heating.

A Simulated Solar Heating Panel

What you need:

- 2 shoe boxes
- plastic wrap
- masking tape
- white paper
- 2 thermometers
- 2 white or light colored cups

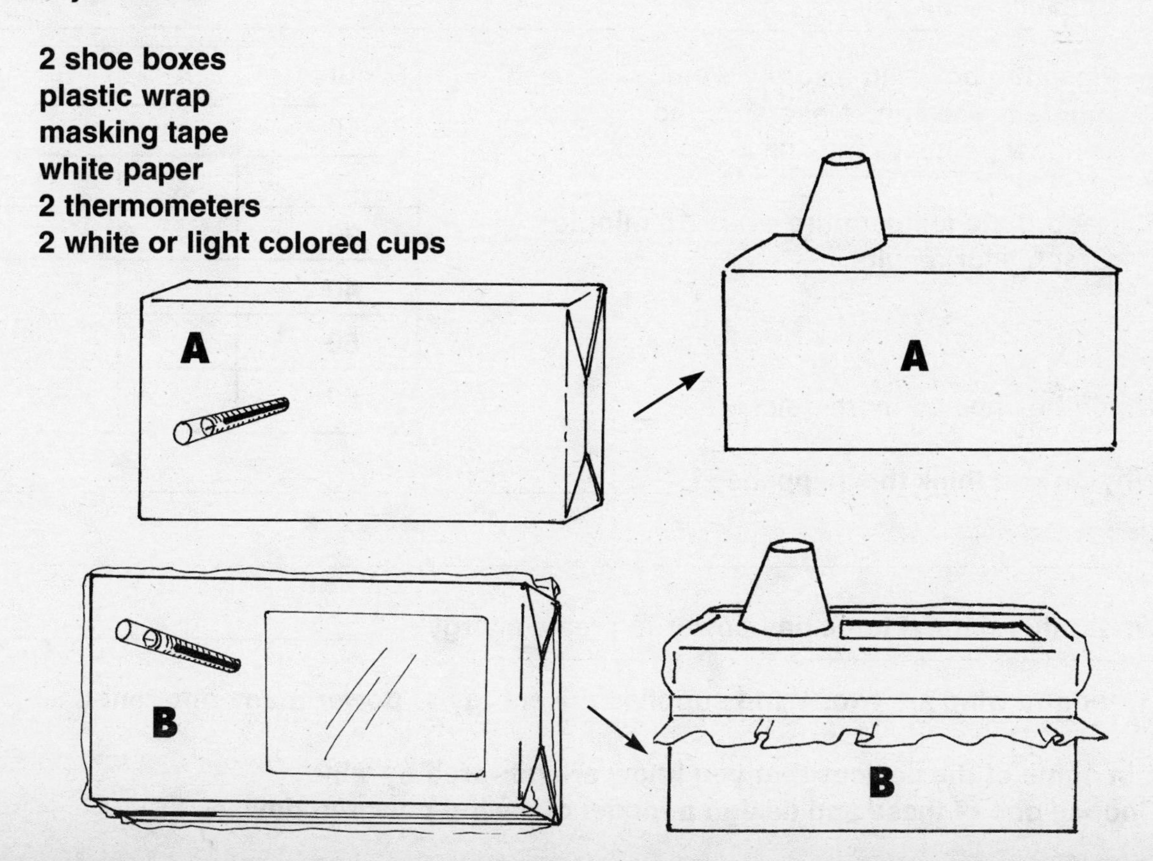

What to do:

1. Cover both boxes with white paper. Mark one box A the other box B.

2. Cut a large window in one of the boxes.

3. Cover the window with plastic wrap and tape the plastic wrap securely to the box.

4. Put a thermometer into the top of each box. Cover each thermometer with a cup of the same light color.

5. Place the boxes in a sunny window so each points to the sun. Make sure the covered window points to the sun.

6. Record the temperature every 10 minutes. Graph your results.

Minutes	A	B
10		
20		
30		
40		
50		
60		

Which box heated more quickly? ____________

Why do you think this happened? ____

____

What other natural force has power to create energy? ______________________

Water and wind are two. Wind supplies the energy to power many different devices.

List some of the devices that you know are powered by wind.
Choose one of these and design a model of a wind powered device.

Weather And The Power Of Wind

Air moves from an area of high pressure to an area of low pressure. This movement is what causes wind. The more extreme the difference between the two pressures, the stronger the wind will be. Air acts a lot like water so we can simulate the movement from high to low pressure with two bottles of water.

Air Movement

What you need:

- scissors
- food coloring
- modeling clay
- water
- plastic tube or a plastic straw
- a pencil
- two 2-liter clear soda bottles
- a marker

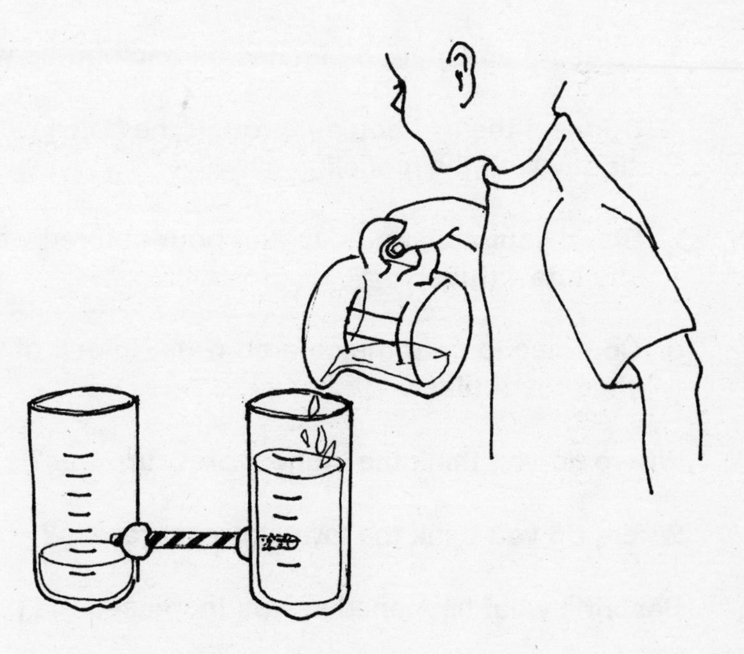

What to do:

1. Ask an adult helper to make a hole about three inches up from the bottom of each bottle. Use scissors to make the holes the correct size. The holes should be large enough for the straw (or tube) to fit in.

2. Ask an adult helper to cut the tops off of each bottle.

3. Measure and mark off inches on each bottle with a marker.

4. Connect the two bottles through the holes with the straw (or tube). Seal the holes tightly with the modeling clay.

5. Stand your apparatus up and pour colored water into both bottles up to just above the straw (tube).

6. Continue to pour the colored water in one of the bottles and watch what happens in the other bottle.

Where do you think the highest pressure was? ____________________

Where do you think the lowest pressure was? ____________________

Describe what happened as you increased the pressure in one bottle.

____

____

____

Air Movement And Friction

The ground can slow air movement. It is friction that can cause the air to slow when it gets close to the ground. You can simulate this action with milk and a soda bottle.

Slow Moving Particles

What you need:

- **2-liter soda bottle**
- **scissors**
- **milk**
- **food coloring**
- **a baking dish**

What to do:

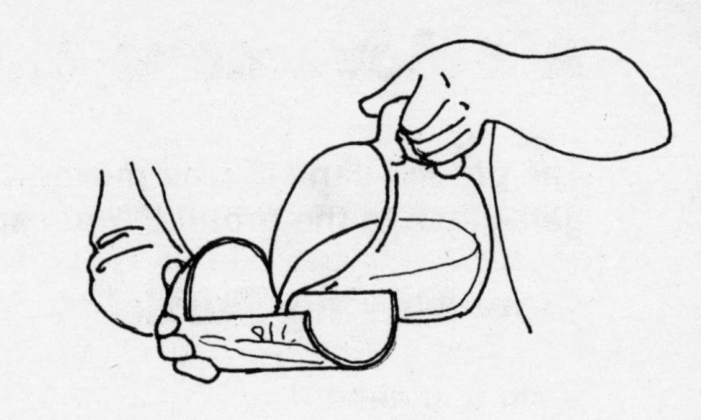

1. Ask an adult helper to cut the bottle into a scoop shape like the one shown.

2. Pour milk into the scoop and hold it so it does not run out yet.

3. Drop several drops of food coloring in the center of the milk puddle. Make a line of food coloring across the milk.

4. Carefully and very slowly tilt the scoop slightly over the pan so the milk slowly begins to flow into the baking pan. Watch the food coloring.

Describe what shape the food coloring takes.
Which part of the food coloring seems to be moving faster? How do you know?

____

____

It is the friction of the milk against the plastic at the sides of the scoop that makes the milk at the sides move more slowly than the milk in the middle.

Describe how this is like air movement against the earth. ______________________

____

____

Air Movement And Temperature

Our air is moving constantly. Do you remember the word "density?" What about the comparison of a two pound frying pan to a two pound pile of cotton balls? What was denser, the frying pan or the cotton balls? What was denser, the water or the oil? Well, when air is warm, it is less dense than colder air. So, when air is warm, it rises and the colder air sinks taking up the space where the warmer air was. Let's see if we can prove that warm air rises.

What you need:

the snake on the next page
heavy construction paper
a heat source such as a radiator or a warm lamp
string
scissors
a helper

What to do:

1. Cut out the snake on the next page.

2. Trace the snake on a piece of heavy construction paper. Color your snake.

3. Put a small hole in the center of the snake's head. Thread the string through the hole and tie a knot in the end of the string.

4. Tell your helper you can make your snake dance just by whistling or humming a tune.

5. Hold the snake above the radiator or lamp. Hum a tune or sing a song. After a few seconds, your snake should start to spin.

   How do you think the spinning of the snake shows that warm air rises?

6. You can make a spinning snake mobile. Trace and color several snakes. Using string and a coat hanger, hang them above a radiator. Whenever the heat goes on, your snake mobile will spin.

Barometers

A barometer measures air pressure. Changing air pressure tells you what kind of weather to expect. Make your own barometer and see if you can become a meteorologist. Do you know what a meteorologist does? If not, how do you think you can find out? Follow your suggestion and write a description of a meteorologist.

A Homemade Barometer

What you need:

- a glass or plastic jar such as an empty peanut butter jar
- a large balloon
- scissors
- rubber bands
- a plastic straw
- glue or rubber cement
- an empty milk or juice carton
- an index card
- paper and pencil

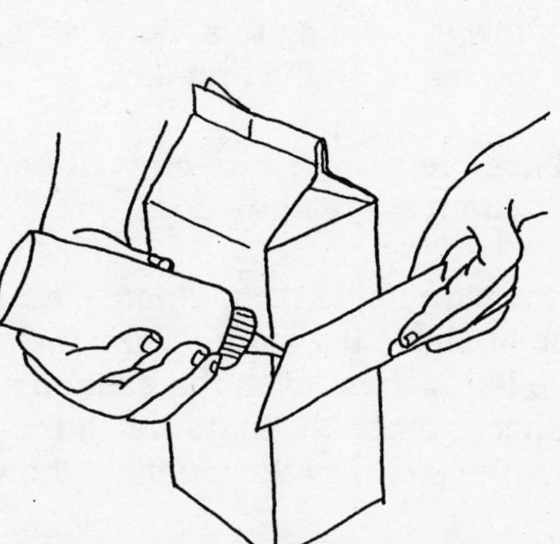

What to do:

1. Cut a piece of the balloon big enough to fit over the mouth of the jar. Stretch the piece over the jar and hold it in place with a rubber band or two.

2. Glue one end of the straw to the middle of the piece of balloon.

3. Glue the index card to the side of the milk carton as shown. Place it on the carton so the straw you glued to the balloon points about to the middle of the card.

4. Put the jar and the milk carton apparatus in a place where the temperature stays pretty much the same. Set them up so the straw points to the middle of the card. Mark that exact spot on the card.

5. Check your barometer every day. Write down on a piece of paper whether the straw is pointing to a higher or a lower spot than the mark you made on the first day.

From time to time, balance the air pressure on your barometer. Do this by removing the balloon and replacing it about every three days.

When the pressure of the air outside the jar increases, it pushes down on the balloon and makes the straw point above the mark. When the pressure on the outside of the jar decreases, the air in the jar pushes up on the balloon and makes the straw point below the mark. Stormy weather is probably on its way if the air pressure outside the jar is less than the pressure inside the jar. Why do you think the word "probably" is important when predicting weather?

A Homemade Thermometer

While you're building tools a meteorologist would use, you might as well build a thermometer, too.

What you need:

- a glass bottle with a small mouth
- a straw
- an eyedropper
- modeling clay
- 3"x5" index card
- red food coloring
- tape
- a weather thermometer
- warm water
- a marker or pen

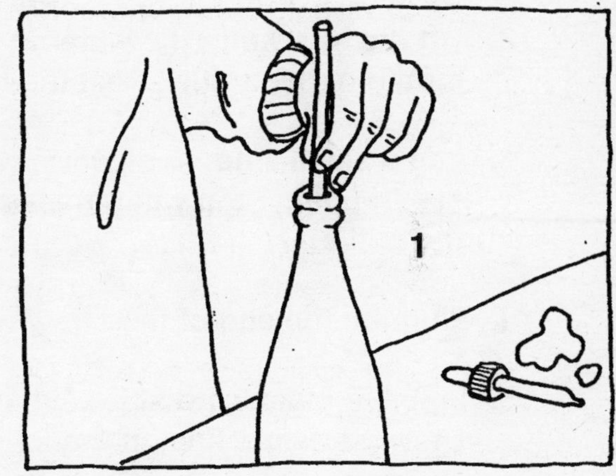

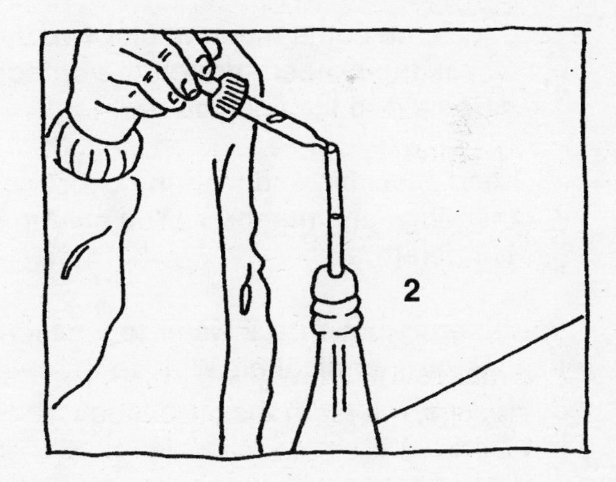

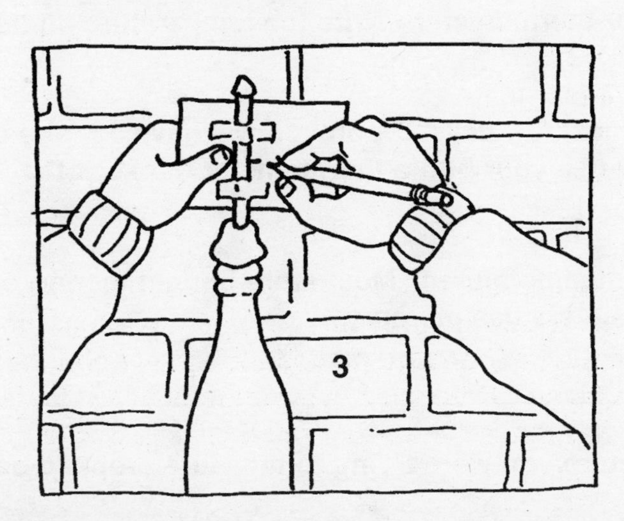

What to do:

1. Fill the bottle all the way to the top with warm water. Add some red food coloring to the water.

2. Put the straw into the water in the bottle. Mold clay firmly around the straw and the mouth of the bottle. Seal the bottle tightly with the clay.

3. Add a small amount of warm red-colored water through the top of the straw with an eyedropper. Stop when the water level in the straw is about an inch above the top of the bottle.

4. Plug the top end of the straw with a tiny stopper made of clay.

5. Tape the index card sideways onto the straw as you see in the picture. Draw a straight line on the card to mark the level of the water in the straw.

6. Check the bottle thermometer two or three hours later. Mark the level again. Check the temperature on the outdoor thermometer. Write the temperature on the card next to the line you drew.

7. Keep checking and marking over the next few days. Soon you will have a range of markings and numbers. You can now use your bottle thermometer to check the temperature.

Your thermometer uses water to measure temperatures. Most store-bought thermometers use mercury or alcohol. Why do thermometers use mercury?

___

(Hint: What would happen if the temperature you were trying to measure dropped below 32 degrees F?)

Francis Beaufort's Scale

If you watch carefully, you can often tell how fast the wind is blowing. That's what Sir Francis Beaufort did. Nearly 200 years ago, he created a scale you can still use to measure wind speed by observing its effect on things around you.

SCALE NUMBER	WIND SPEED (MILES PER HOUR)	WHAT TO OBSERVE
0	under 1	Smoke rises straight up.
1	1 to 3	Smoke drifts.
2	4 to 7	Leaves on trees rustle. You feel wind on your face.
3	8 to 12	Flags flap. Paper and leaves blow on the ground.
4	13 to 18	Paper and leaves are blown into the air.
5	19 to 24	Small trees sway.
6	25 to 31	Flags flap. Hats blow off. Umbrellas are hard to use.
7	32 to 38	Large trees move. People have difficulty walking into the wind.
8	39 to 46	Twigs snap off trees. Walking into the wind is nearly impossible.
9	47 to 54	Branches break off trees. Shingles fly off roofs.
10	55 to 63	Trees are uprooted. Buildings are damaged.
11	64 to 75	Violent winds cause serious property damage.
12	over 75	Hurricane!

Watch The Wind

Just For Fun

You can turn a cereal box into a kind of camera. Point it out the window and you will see a miniature picture show right inside the box.

Cereal Box Camera

What you need:

an empty cereal box
scissors
wax paper
a pin
tape

What to do:

1. Measure your cereal box to make sure it is at least 12 inches tall. Remove the wax paper from the inside and throw it away.

2. You must now make a flap in the box. It should look just like the picture on page 116. Take your scissors and cut across the middle of the box. Now cut down one side. finally cut across the bottom so the flap opens.

3. Take a smooth piece of wax paper that is about two inches high. Tape both sides so the paper is standing two inches from the bottom of the box. Be sure there are no wrinkles or creases in your wax paper. The smoother the piece, the better the camera will work.

4. Close the flap and tape it shut so that no light can get inside.

5. Using a pin, carefully poke a tiny hole in the middle of the bottom of your box.

6. Cut off the top flaps of the box. Shape the top of the box so your face will fit snugly against it. It is a good idea to cut a space for your nose.

7. Hold the box up to your eyes and point the pinhole out the window on a sunny day. Cup your hands so that as little light gets inside as possible. Light must enter only through the pinhole you made! If light leaks through the cracks in your box, cut up a brown paper bag and wrap it around the outside of your camera.

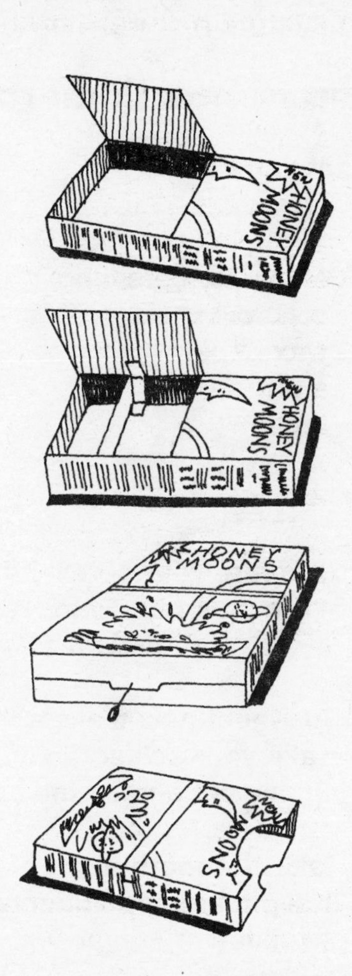

You should see a miniature upside-down picture inside the box. Light rays enter your box only through the pinhole. They fall on the wax paper to make a little picture or image of what's outside. Light rays travel in straight lines. Those that come from low objects outside hit near the top of the wax paper. Those from high objects outside hit near the bottom of the wax paper. So the image is upside down.

You have built a device called a camera obscura. It has been used for centuries by artists and astronomers to project images of things they wish to see.

Mirror Darts

You can play darts at light-speed if the darts are rays of light. You and your friends can hit a target with light rays again and again, using only mirrors.

What you need:

- two partners
- two mirrors
- a small flashlight
- a piece of paper
- a pencil or pen
- tape
- a dark room

What to do:

1. Draw a target on the piece of paper and tape it to a wall.
2. Give each of your partners a mirror.
3. Turn off the lights and turn on the flashlight.
4. Shine the flashlight at the first mirror and watch the light bounce off. Have your partners try to bounce the light reflection off their mirrors onto the target.
5. Keep shifting position until you find your target. Practice until the three of you hit the target.
6. Change positions and try again.

Hand Shadows

Hand shadow-like animals are easy to make and lots of fun. All you need are your hands, some idea of what animals look like, a wall and a bright light. Be careful handling the light source. Remember a bulb gets very hot.

What you need:

a lamp
a dark room
your hands
imagination
a paper and pencil

What to do:

1. Hold your hands between the light source and the wall.

2. Here are some ideas to start with. If you have a partner, have your partner guess what the animal is.

3. Have your partner hold paper up on the wall and make your shadows on the paper. Have your partner draw around the shadow and the two of you can create wonderful new creatures. Have fun with this project. And have fun with science, too!

Does Science Really Affect You?

It's fun to read about discoveries and talk about inventions. But does science really mean anything to you and your every day life? Think about the most important inventions of the past few centuries. What about the car, the light bulb, telephone, the television, computers. Are any of these part of your every day life? What about antibiotics, vitamins, new medical equipment?

Now, think about the future. What role do you think science will play in the future? Today we face some difficult decisions about things like the environment, hunger, social issues, and the global community. The future -your future- will turn to science more and more to find the solutions to problems and answers to many new questions that are certain to rise. Here are a few problems to start you practicing your problem-solving process.

What you need:

a science journal
some problems to solve
an imagination and inquisitive mind
access to research sources such as a library, experts, a computer, or computer software

What to do:

1. Define the problem: What am I trying to find out?
2. Gather evidence: What do I already know? What do I need to find out?
3. Make a prediction: What do I think will happen?
4. Experiment: How can I test my prediction?
5. Gather results: What did my experiment show?
6. Draw a conclusion: What did I learn about the problem? Did I find possible ways to solve the problem?
7. Raise new questions: What do I still not understand? What new problem does my conclusion cause?

How Can People Use The Sun For Energy?

The Sun is a good source of energy. Some people are already using solar energy. "Solar" means from the sun. People in some places use this energy to heat their homes and their water. Using solar energy helps us save oil, natural gas, and coal.

People collect the sun's energy in flat, black boxes on their roofs. The boxes are black because dark colors absorb the energy better. The black boxes have water in them. The sun heats the water. The water may be used for bathing or washing, or pumped through the house to keep the house warm.

Solar energy can also be used to generate electricity. Some watches and calculators run on solar energy. We are unlikely to run out of solar energy as a source of energy. What are some ways solar energy can be used so we can save other resources like oil, natural gas, and coal? What are some questions you have about energy sources? What is some information that might help you design ways to use solar energy?

How Are Germs In Food Harmful?

Some germs that grow in food can be harmful to us. Bacteria grow slowly in something that is cold, but can multiply quickly when the temperature gets warmer. Cooked food that has been left out for a long time is a perfect place for bacteria to grow. These bacteria produce poisons, or toxins, that attack your cells and make you sick. This is called food poisoning.

Sometimes a harmful toxin can grow in canned food. As these bacteria grow, they produce gas. Never eat food from a can that has a bump or bulge. The bump or bulge may have been caused from this dangerous gas.

What do you know? What do you need to find out? How will you find information about this problem? Decide how to avoid eating bacteria that might be in foods. Decide and explain how to solve the problem of illness caused by these bacteria. What are some of the things you can do everyday to keep your body healthy?

Is Your Food Real Or Synthetic? Does It Matter?

Imagine ice cream with no fat. Almost 40 % of the calories that Americans ingest come from fat. American's use of artificial sweetener each year equals about 20 pounds of sugar per person. Many food chemists believe synthetic foods are the answer to health problems. Using chemical substances mixed in certain ways, scientist can create a "fake-fat" with neither calories nor cholesterol. Used in foods like cheesecake and ice cream, this fake-fat tastes pretty similar to real fat but is not absorbed into the body as natural fat is.

Some scientists feel there is a need to worry. Some tests of synthetic foods have shown some may cause headaches and mood swings. Also, some scientists have concerns about long-term effects of synthetic foods. What do you think? Make a plan for finding out more information about synthetic foods, what they are, how scientists are testing them, how food companies are using them. What are some questions you have about the pros and cons of synthetic food?

Why Has The Human Life Span Increased?

Many life cycles exist in nature. You are probably most familiar with your own – the human life cycle. But what you may not know is how much the average number of years a person lives has increased and continues to increase. In the early years of human history, most people did not live much beyond 30 years of age. Death often resulted from disease, improper diet, and the lack of medicines and medical knowledge available today.

Today, people can expect to live into their 70s, even into their 80s and beyond due to changes in sanitation, the way we prepare and store food, human diet, health practices, and medical technology to prevent diseases. Modern technology has greatly increased the life span of people in the developed countries of the world. However, much still needs to be done in many undeveloped and developing countries to provide good health practices, proper diets, and medical service. What problem can you identify in what you just read? What are some things you already know? What are some questions you have? How can you find answers to these questions? What are some solutions you can come up with to solve the problem you identified?

Graphic Organizers

Graphic Organizers do exactly what their name suggests. These graphs and charts help you organize information for clarity, to better understand concepts, or to organize information for reference later. Use these Graphic Organizers to help you organize what you are learning. Each type of Graphic Organizer shown contains an example of how it can be used.

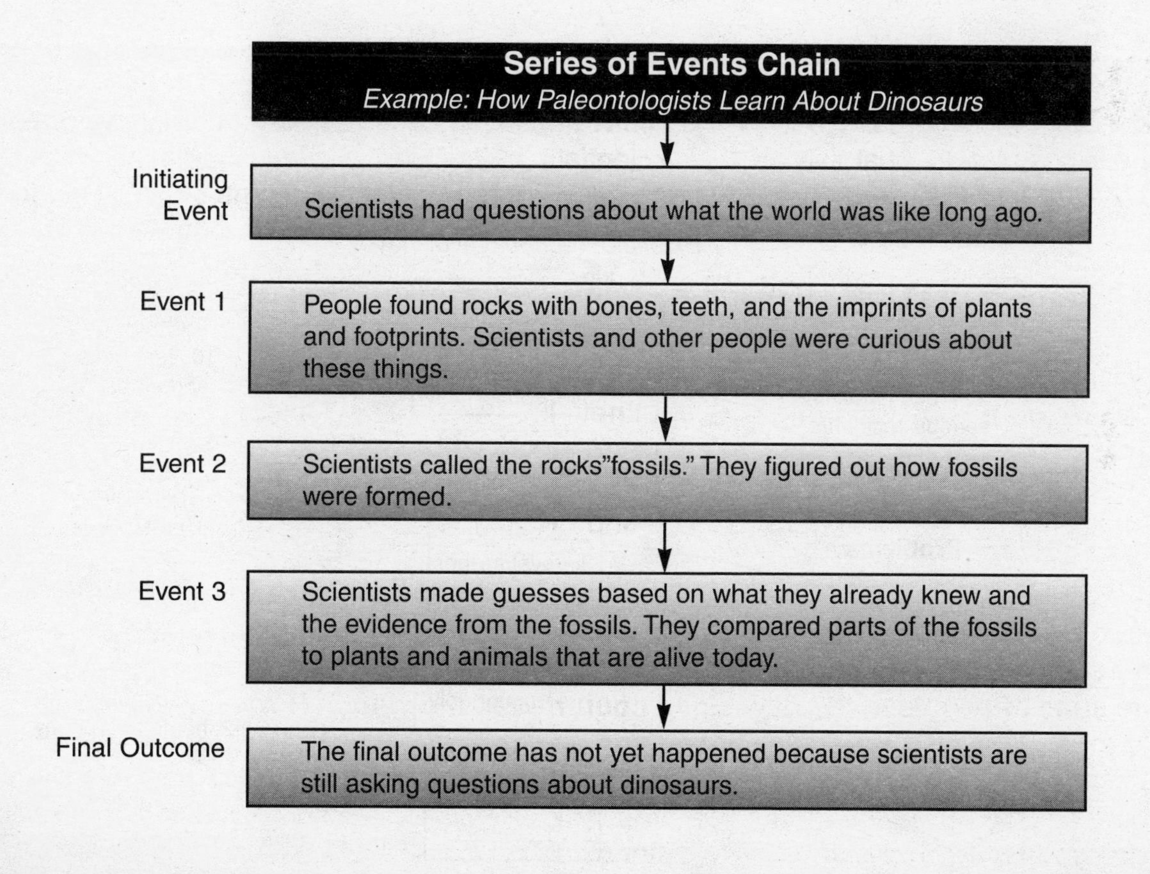

Venn Diagram

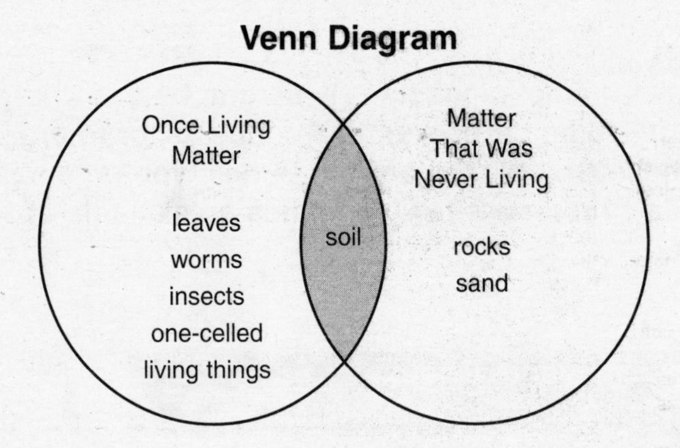

Spiral Map

Example: Technology of Travel

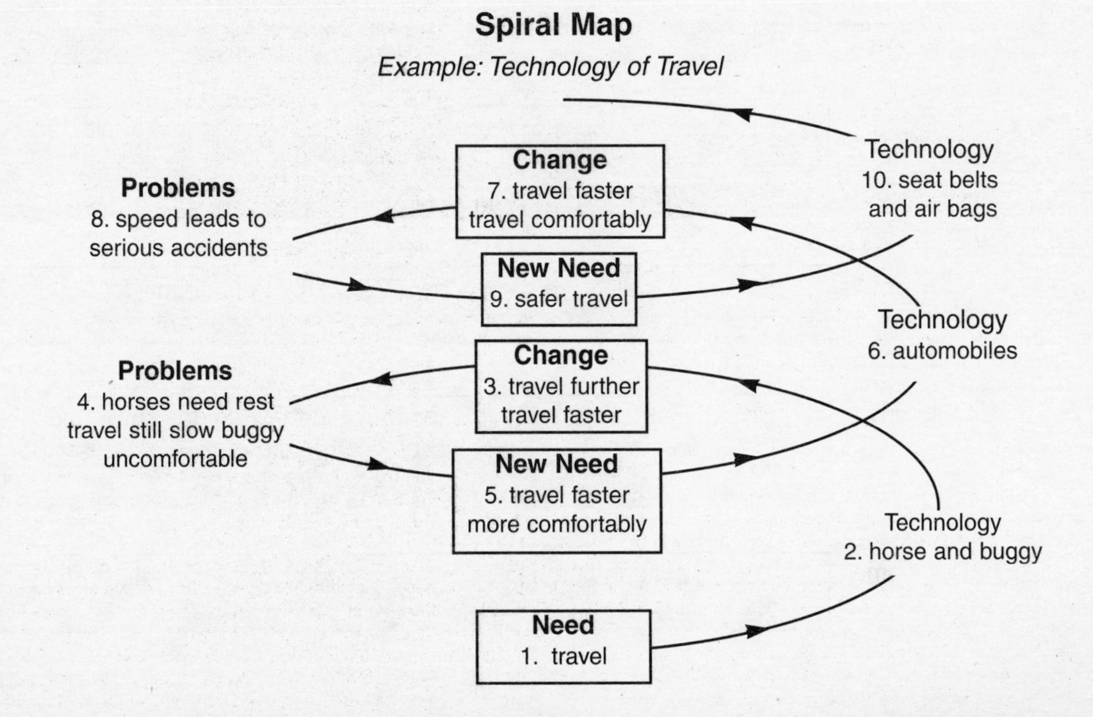

Answers

Remember, accept any reasonable response. Children should be encouraged to be creative. If they come up with an interesting response, check it out together.

Page
10. botanist-scientist who studies plants; cartographer-map maker; geologist-scientist who studies the Earth, especially its rocks; paleontologist -scientist who studies the life of the past through fossils and fossil remains; mechanical engineer-a professional who designs machines; ecologist-scientist who studies environments, especially the interrelationships of organisms and their environment; anatomist-scientist who studies the anatomy; inventor-scientist or other professional who creates new tools and machines; astronomer-scientist who studies the celestial bodies, their movement, mass, and composition. Other scientists might include chemist, anthropologist, archeologist, physicist, meteorologist, zoologist, entomologist, herpetologist, geneticist. There are many different sciences. Accept any reasonable responses. Verify responses with reference books.

11. Certainly, a great deal has yet to be discovered in all areas of science including the study of dinosaurs, fossils, evolution.

12. You probably have been doing investigations and experiments for several years that utilize some or all of these steps.

14. Accept any reasonable response. Remember people are living organisms. Responses may include pets, insects, spiders, birds, reptiles, amphibians, fish, mammals; trees, flowering plants, conifers, ferns, horsetails, moss, algae, liverworts.

15. The plant cell has a cell wall and chloroplasts. The plant cell model seems firmer. The animal cell seems more malleable. The plant and animal cells both have a nucleus, mitochondria, and cell membranes.

16. This is a good place to start a science journal. Also, have available a good dictionary and access to good reference materials. Remember, the onion skin must be only one cell layer thin to be able to see an individual cell.

18. Remember the dictionary. A cell membrane is the thin plasma membrane that surround cells. It has pores to allow some materials to enter and leave the cell. Since it allows only some substances to enter and leave it is called semipermeable.

19. Potato #2 is the potato with living cells and sugar in the hole. After one day water should have accumulated in the hole. This shows that water passes through the living cells from the dish into the hole where the sugar was. Potato #1 does not have the sugar in the hole so not as much water will accumulate in the hole because less water is osmosing from lesser substance to greater substance. Also, Potato #3 will have less water in the hole even though there is sugar in the hole because water does not move through dead cells in the same way it moves through living cells. The most water will have moved through the living cells to the greater amount of sugar placed in the hole-Potato #2.

23. The root should begin growing in the opposite direction again-down as a result of gravity. The roots should be in the soil and the leaves/stems above in the light.

25. Plant # 1 should begin growing upward toward the cut out window. The leaf(ves) will be facing the cutout window. Plant #2 will show some growth around the dividers. The leaves will be winding their way upward in response to the light. Plant #3 has no obstruction to the sunlight so its leaves will probably be growing randomly with the tops of the leaves facing the sunlight. The plants are each responding to the light that is available to them. Plants like these should be planted where they can obtain some direct sunlight during the day.

26. Responses will vary. Accept any reasonable responses. Trees grow around buildings, highway barriers, playground equipment, other larger trees and plants.

27. Accept any reasonable responses. Remember, trees that grow about one inch each year to their circumference include trees like maple trees, some fruit trees, elm trees, and oak trees. Palms grow taller faster than they grow wider and yews and chestnuts don't grow an inch to their circumference each year. So check the tree you are measuring. Since many trees grow one inch each year to their circumference, a tree with a circumference of 15 inches is approximately 15 years old. This should be easy to calculate. The circumference is the length around the tree. Diameter is the length across the tree through the middle of the tree. Relative to means in relation to. Here's an example. You are tall "relative to" a tulip. But you are short "relative to" a 200' redwood tree. Use the dictionary.

29. Different colors would be variables. The color should not have much effect although the intensity of color will make the effect more dramatic. The water is diffusing through the cell walls and cell membranes to fill up the plant cells. As the plant cells fill, the turgor pressure increases. The plant cells are like the balloon. With less water, they do not have pressure to stand the plant firmly but filled with water, the plant stands firmly and the turgor pressure is strong enough to stand the plant up. The balloon simulates water pressure but is not a living organism such as a plant cell and does not have a permeable or semipermeable membrane. Water does not osmose through the balloon as it does through a living plant cell.

30. Accept all reasonable experimental designs. Make sure the "What you need:" list is complete and the "What to do:" steps are clear and thorough. Try out the experiment. Make sure nothing in the experiment is dangerous. Applaud creativity.

31. Water will begin accumulating on the inside of the clear plastic bag. The water evaporates through the stomata of the leaves. Humidity is the amount of water in the air. Humidity affects how temperature feels. 80 degrees F seems hotter when the air is humid or contains more moisture/water. Humidity indexes indicate how the humidity or amount of the moisture in the air affects the results of high or low temperatures. Usually weather reports in newspapers or on TV give the humidity and/or heat indexes.

Answers

Page

32. Accept any reasonable experimental designs. Make sure the "What you need:" list is complete and the "What to do:" steps are clear and thorough. Try out the experiment. Make sure nothing in the experiment is dangerous. Applaud creativity.

34. Since water cannot evaporate through the layer of oil, all evaporation that is measured must result from the water moving up the stem, into the leaf, and through the stomata. The water level in the jar with no oil may be lower. This results from the evaporation of the water directly from the jar to the air. The level of water in the jar with oil measures only the water that was absorbed into the stems and evaporated through the leaves.

35. The grass under the pot will be yellowed or beginning to yellow. The grass around the pot will be greener than the grass under the pot. When the grass could not capture the sunlight, it could not make more chlorophyll. As it used up the chlorophyll available, it could not make more without the presence of sunlight.

36. Obtain a good reference book about animals.

40-42. Animals and signs of animals will vary depending on where you live. Be very observant. Signs of animals are not always obvious. Chewed leaves or half eaten nuts and berries don't stand out. Spider webs and paths are often very small and subtle. Nests are hidden in trees and under overhangs. Eggs and shells may be hidden. Listen for sounds of animals and note that pets are often overlooked. So be very observant.

43-44. Remember to respect animals, all animals. Be very careful not to harm them. Make sure they get enough air and return them to their natural environment. The word "bug" should give away the fact that they may find very small insects and/or spiders. The kinds of animals in the soil will depend on location. Obtain a good reference book about animals in your environment. A pet store or conservancy also has good references.

45. The sunlight zone.

46. Buoy is a floating warning or directional system for boats. Buoyancy is the tendency to rise or float when submerged in liquid. People use life preservers. Remember, da Vinci invented a life saver. Actually our lungs do help us float to a certain extent. But the weight of the rest of our bodies drags us down. Accept any reasonable responses. Some people inflate large balloons under ships or other objects to float them to the surface. Make a submarine with a soda bottle. You can sink it then blow air through a straw to raise it again.

48. The bottom hole should squirt out the farthest because the pressure is greater deeper in the cup. The top hole will squirt out the shortest. At this depth, the pressure is the least.

49. Integrated in this context means the sciences and processes form and blend into a functioning or unified whole and do not stand alone and are not studied alone. We do not learn only one curricula at a time.

49. Learning is a composite of skills, processes, and content. In most cases, we are learning information in order to solve problems and find new solutions. Learning and problem solving help us in our daily life and our daily life is integrated with math, social studies, social needs, science, language arts, music, art, physical education, health, and all areas of the curricula.

50-51. The temperature of the thermometer in the cup with cotton balls and oil should not have decreased as much as the temperature of the thermometer without the oil. The oil acts as an insulator from the cold. The oil simulates the layer of fat called blubber in whales. Just as the oil insulation kept the heat in the thermometer in the freezer, the blubber in a whale keeps the warmth inside the whale. Birds and Mammals are warm-blooded animals. Most other animals are cold-blooded.

53. The magma that flows out as lava contains liquid and solid materials from inside the mantle. Volcanoes offer information such as the extremity of heat, the movement of liquid and solid materials within the Earth, the reactions of moving plates. The study of earthquakes, volcanoes, and the structure of Earth's rocks and minerals really give us most of the information we know about Earth and will give us more information in the future.

54-55. In this activity margarine or butter simulates magma. When it is not heated, it is solid as magma is. But when it is warmed it becomes more fluid and moves as a liquid moves. As the butter or margarine warms, the molecules begin to move more than the cooler molecules. This makes the butter or margarine fluid and move in a similar fashion as molten liquid magma.

56-57. Density is a difficult concept to grasp. The best way to appreciate density is through analogies. The analogy to a frying pan and cotton balls. Other examples might include feathers and a bowling ball. How many feathers would it take to weigh as much as a bowling ball? How much space would that number of feathers take up compared to the space a bowling balls takes up? Magma is less dense than the ground and materials around it so it rises to the surface. The magma is similar to the oil in that the oil is less dense than the water and thus floats or rises to the surface of the water. The oil may break up into smaller globules but will not mix with the water. The oil is less dense. It will float or rise to the surface if left to settle. The magma is more like the oil and the water more like the rock.

58-59. Be careful with this experiment. Stand back from the potato plug. Remember, this is only a simulation of the power that builds to unplug a volcano. The vinegar and baking soda will cause a chemical reaction in which carbon dioxide is produced. Enough gas will be produced to "blow" the potato plug off the mouth of the bottle.

61. When you move your hand in the same direction as you moved the sandpaper, the wood should feel smooth. But when you move your hand in the opposite direction as the direction you sandpapered, the surface of the wood will feel rougher. Be careful not to get any splinters.

63. A seismometer is a tool that contains a weight so heavy that it stays still while everything else around it shakes. Levers record the shaking on a drum. The shakes recorded then are measured and compared.

Answers

Page

63. A good reference source such as the internet, the library, or an expert. Usually meteorologists can describe tools such as the seismometer.

64. Each of the towels or rugs simulates a plate. As the rugs or towels push toward each other they begin folding on themselves. The folds build simulated "mountain ranges."

67. The balloon should stick to the wall. The balloon, like the comb, attracted the positive parts of the atoms in the paper confetti. The friction between the hair and the balloon and the hair and the comb produced the static electricity. When you walk across a carpet and touch something; when you put a freshly washed and dried sweater on over your head; when a skirt or shirt sticks to you-not because of sweat.

69. You can use the copper wire without the penny as long as you also have a paper clip. It may be difficult to see the light. Keep trying. Another way to determine you produced electricity with your lemon is by touching your tongue to the wire. You can feel a slight tingling sensation. Get energy from other kinds of food such as banana, milk, peanut butter, etc. by eating them. This was sort of a trick question since these foods do not contain citric acid such as lemons.

70. Be very careful with this experiment. Steam can burn quickly.

74. As the heat hits the blades, the turbine fan will begin turning. The more heat, the faster the fan will turn. The blades will turn the direction they are angled. As steam turns the fan in a real steam turbine, the fan turns a generator that generates electricity. The heat from the radiator or heating vent simulates the steam engine.

76. Accept any reasonable responses. Applaud creativity. Wires with three-pronged plugs are usually larger in circumference and/or diameter. Usually appliances with three-pronged plugs and larger wires require more electricity to function. Remember, always make sure to use only a three-pronged outlet for a three-pronged plug.

77. Accept any reasonable designs of a series circuit. The diagrammed circuit should show the symbols for two "power sources, one switch, and two light bulbs.

78. + indicates positive and - indicates negative. The metal spring holds the batteries tightly in place so there is a good connection with the metal strip that is running along the side from bottom to top of the flashlight case. There is a small wire inside the light bulb. The wire is the continuation of the circuit and the part that glows. The base of the bulb is metal also so the circuit is continuous.

79. Accept any reasonable illustrations. Make sure there are batteries, a light bulb, continuous metal circuit, and a switch. The switch connects and disconnects the circuit. When the switch connects the circuit, the light shines. When the switch disconnects or breaks the circuit, the light goes out.

80. If the lights in a home were connected in a series circuit, they would all go out when the switch disconnected or broke the circuit. Accept any reasonable diagram. Make sure there are three lights, at least one switch, and at least one power source. There should be only one power source. However, the design may show more than one switch.

81. <u>Get her away from the socket.</u> Take the keys away immediately. Tell an adult about the situation. Ask an adult to find a safety plug or get one yourself and put the safety plug in the outlet.
<u>Check on your dad.</u> If he is in shock or passed out, call for another adult and call 911 immediately. Make sure you and he are both away from the electrical current. Use CPR appropriately if you've been trained.
<u>Don't ever put anything in the toaster except bread.</u> A toaster can cause both a bad shock and a bad burn. Unplug the toaster. Ask an adult for help.

82. Make sure home is safe. If any problems show up on this check list, work to solve those problems.

87. The amount of oil retrieved will depend on the apparatus. However, the point here is that it will take several pumpings to get most of the oil out of the marble/pebble, bottle. Warm water will help some but there will probably still be some amount of oil left in the bottle. Oil wells also have rocks and stones in them like the pebbles and/or marbles. It is difficult to retrieve oil from a well just as it was difficult to retrieve the oil from the bottle. It is almost impossible to get all the oil out of the bottle just as it is very difficult to clean all the oil from an accidental spill. Ideas for cleaning oil will vary but applaud creativity. Some of the work done recently in Alaska and in Europe will offer some ideas to cleaning oil spills. Better safety measures should be taken with transporting fossil fuels. Accept any reasonable responses about safety measures that can be taken.

88. Fossil Fuel Network Tree

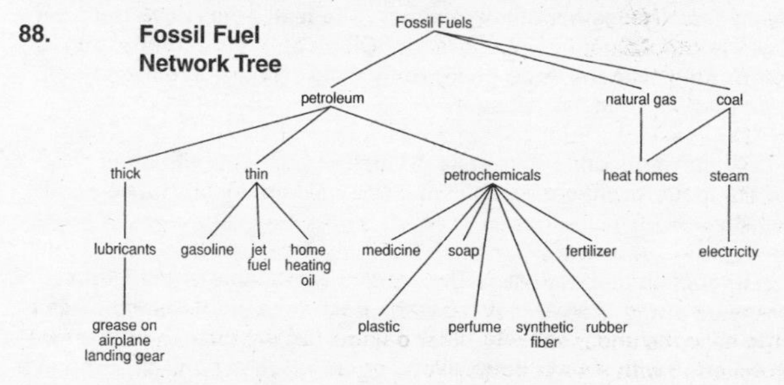

89. Greenhouses are also called hothouses and are used by farmers and gardeners to grow plants even when the climate outside is not suitable. Greenhouses maintain a hot humid climate by using glass or Plexiglas to magnify and retain the sun's heat. The greenhouse effect is an environmental problem being caused by the burning of fossil fuels. The more carbon dioxide and carbon monoxide that enters the atmosphere, the more the sun's heat energy is trapped in our atmosphere.

Answers

Page

89. Too much greenhouse gas could cause the Earth to warm. The warmer the Earth gets, the more problems can occur such as melting polar regions and icebergs, increased temperatures that affect weather, decreased rain, flooding, erosion.

90. The temperature in the box with the plastic wrap increased because the plastic wrap trapped the sun's heat in the box. The plastic wrap simulates the layer of greenhouse gases that trap the sun's heat energy in the Earth's atmosphere. You can start a greenhouse anywhere and in any environment. A box with a clear plastic cover works well to start a herb garden. Accept any reasonable design ideas. Build the greenhouse design and start a greenhouse.

91. People living in very cold places could begin growing crops for food. Trees and crops could be ruined. People's homes could be destroyed. Plants, animals, and people would not have enough water to survive in those places. Accept any reasonable predictions.

92-93. Some oil can be separated from the water by pouring. However, this is almost impossible in nature since you can't really pour oil out of the ocean. Filters and skims can be used to pick up the oil. The sand stays separate from the water. The water and oil stay separate but the oil covers the sand grains. The baking soda mixed with the water. The vinegar formed with the baking soda to produce carbon dioxide. The vinegar simulates acid pollution. The sand simulates solid pollution as well as natural soil. The oil simulates fossil fuel pollution. The vinegar and baking soda mixed to cause a chemical reaction. The bubbles show that a new substance was produced.

94. The feather placed in the clean water will dry easily and move gently in the breeze. When the feather is placed in the oil, the oil coats the feather and it becomes heavy. It does not dry and the oil sticks to the feather and keeps the feather stuck together. The feather is heavy from the oil and does not move gently in the breeze. Oil on animals in nature can close their pours, make them too heavy to fly or to swim, clog gills, poison them, make them sink and drowned.

95. There were dangerous leaks of nuclear waste at both sites. The results of the most recent catastrophe at Chernobyl are still occurring and still being studied.

96. Response time will vary. The second experiment should knock the dominoes down in at least half the time. Each time more dominoes can be knocked down by one, the faster all will fall. This is a chain reaction and the more dominoes, the faster the chain reaction.

98.

	Nuclear Fission	Fossil Fuels
Raw Material	Uranium	coal, natural gas, petroleum
Recyclable	NO	NO
Pollution	radioactive	greenhouse gases
Safety	can be dangerous	resulting pollution can be dangerous
Unlimited Supply	NO	NO

98. Responses will vary. The sun, wind, nuclear fusion, energy conservation are some other resolutions.

100. The box with the plastic wrap should heat faster. The white paper reflects the sun. The plastic wrap absorbs the sun's heat energy thus increasing the temperature within that box. Water and wind can both be used as natural energy resources. Accept any reasonable design and build the designed tools.

102. The highest pressure will be in the bottle with the most water. The lowest pressure will be in the bottle with the least water. As the pressure in the bottle with the most water increased, the water moved through the straw to an area of lesser pressure. Eventually the two bottles of water will equalize.

104. The food coloring will take the shape of a v. The coloring in the center will move faster than the color closer to the sides of the scoop. The friction of the milk against the scoop sides slows the milk. The milk simulates air. When air is close to the ground, the friction between the air and the ground will slow the movement of air.

106. The radiator heats the air above it. The warm air rises, and cooler air rushes in to take its place. Then that air warms and rises, too. This cycle of moving air keeps your snake spinning. Compare this experiment to the turbine fan you built earlier. How are they the same? How are they different?

109-110. A meteorologist is a scientist who studies and "attempts" to predict weather. When you first put the balloon piece on the jar, the pressure of the air inside the jar is the same as the pressure of the air outside the jar. When the pressure of the air outside increases, it presses down on the balloon. The end of the straw that is glued to the balloon goes down, and the other end goes up. This tells you that clear weather is ahead. When the air pressure on the outside of the jar decreases, the straw moves the other way. Stormy weather is on its way. Air temperature will affect your results. That's why it's important to keep your barometer in a place where the temperature doesn't change very much. Probably is a good word because weather can change. Air masses and currents can change direction so the kind of weather predicted may not come to pass.

112. Alcohol and mercury have a lower freezing point than water and a higher boiling point than water. Water in a thermometer would freeze at 32 degrees F.